EXPLORING

CORNISH

MINES

First published 1994 by

LANDFALL PUBLICATIONS

Landfall, Penpol, Devoran, Truro, Cornwall TR3 6NW
Telephone Truro (0872) 862581

A CIP catalogue record for this book is available from the British Library.

ISBN 1 873443 17 X

ACKNOWLEDGEMENTS

We are grateful to the following people, who have contributed information,
maps or photographs, or checked sections of the text, or both:
Dr Lesley Atkinson, Tony Brooks, Clive Carter, Bryan Earl,
Richard Haszard, Adrian Katsikides, Rose Lewis, Eric Rabjohns,
Cedric Rogers and Lieut. Commdr. P. G. H. Richardson.

Typesetting and maps (other than where acknowledged) by Bob Acton.
All photographs, except where stated to the contrary,
are from the authors' collections.

Printed by the Troutbeck Press
and bound by R. Booth Ltd., Antron Hill, Mabe, Penryn, Cornwall

Kenneth Brown
&
Bob Acton

EXPLORING

CORNISH

MINES

Landfall Publications

Kenneth Brown (shown left near Taylor's Shaft, Tywarnhayle Mine) spent his boyhood in Exeter where he developed an early interest in steam railways. Sent to Cornwall on an engineering course after leaving school, he became fascinated by the three mighty beam engines then still at work at South Crofty and East Pool mines. There followed a brief spell in the army and 12 years in industry before joining the editorial staff of the celebrated journal *Engineering* in 1960. At the end of his career in technical journalism he edited a construction periodical in the Thomson Organisation, from whom he took early retirement in 1988 to pursue more actively researches on the Cornish beam engine. He has written numerous articles, and his advice is constantly sought on engine histories, the conservation of engine houses and the interpretation of mine ruins. He has been a volunteer driver with the Kew Bridge Steam Museum since it opened in 1975 and still visits London regularly to work on the large Cornish engines preserved under steam there.

Bob Acton, born in Sussex and bred mostly in Lincolnshire, is a graduate of Durham University. He has lived in Cornwall since 1967, when he was appointed Head of English at Falmouth Grammar School (Falmouth School from 1971). Since retiring from teaching in 1986 he has written and published a series of guide books founded on the belief that the best way to "discover" Cornwall is on foot. The physical evidence of the County's fascinating industrial history is a focus of attention in all these books, and he tries to atone for his lack of technical knowledge by involving people like Kenneth Brown in their composition. Landfall Publications, named from his house overlooking the site of the old lead- and tin-smelter at Penpol near Devoran, now has a list of over 20 Cornish titles by several authors, including two by Bob's wife, Viv. Bob contributes articles on walking and other subjects such as book and music reviews to several journals, and frequently leads guided walks for local organisations.

CONTENTS

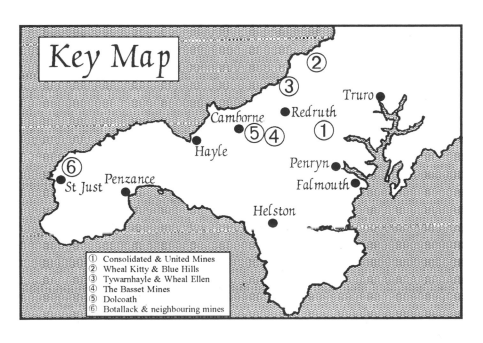

Key Map

① Consolidated & United Mines
② Wheal Kitty & Blue Hills
③ Tywarnhayle & Wheal Ellen
④ The Basset Mines
⑤ Dolcoath
⑥ Botallack & neighbouring mines

IMPORTANT NOTE ON RIGHTS OF WAY
AND ACCESS TO SITES

The walk directions in this book are printed in *italic script*, with the aim of helping the reader to distinguish them from the descriptions and explanations of mining features. The authors have taken pains to make the directions as clear and accurate as possible, and to keep to rights of way wherever practicable. Occasionally, where there was no apparent alternative, footpaths have been included which are clearly in frequent use by the public but not officially designated as rights of way. Paths of this sort are indicated in the text with the symbol #. Please also bear in mind that nothing in the countryside is wholly static, and the condition of paths and tracks - as well as of such features as mine buildings and shafts - is liable to change, sometimes very suddenly. For reasons of safety you should obviously keep to the well-worn paths wherever possible, especially in areas where mining has taken place.

The question of ownership of the mine sites visited in this book is a complex one. Several belong to local authorities (Cornwall County or Districts) or to the National Trust, but parts of others may be in private ownership. Although in practice you are unlikely to be challenged if you explore the areas described - apart from any sections clearly fenced off or marked private - the responsibility for where you go is ultimately your own.

NOTE ON THE MAPS IN THIS BOOK

The walk maps have been drawn to give general guidance of the routes but they do not purport to be precisely to scale or to depict in great detail either the paths to be followed or the various mining features to see on the way. For these it is necessary to keep referring to the text.

Readers wishing to consult large-scale maps of the mining areas traversed by the walks are referred to the Local Studies Library at Clinton Road, Redruth (phone 0209-216760). 1st and 2nd edition Ordnance Survey maps at 25 inches to the mile are held on microfilm (respective dates are 1878 and 1906 or thereabouts), together with up-to-date 6-inch maps.

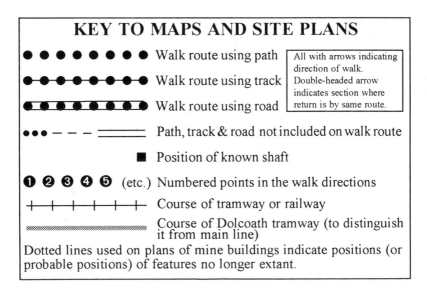

KEY TO MAPS AND SITE PLANS

● ● ● ● ● ● ● Walk route using path

●━●━●━●━● Walk route using track

▰▰▰▰▰▰ Walk route using road

All with arrows indicating direction of walk. Double-headed arrow indicates section where return is by same route.

●●● ─ ─ ─ ═══ Path, track & road not included on walk route

■ Position of known shaft

❶ ❷ ❸ ❹ ❺ (etc.) Numbered points in the walk directions

┼┼┼┼┼┼ Course of tramway or railway

▨▨▨▨▨▨ Course of Dolcoath tramway (to distinguish it from main line)

Dotted lines used on plans of mine buildings indicate positions (or probable positions) of features no longer extant.

INTRODUCTION

Rambling over old mines is a highly pleasurable pastime. It offers all the relaxing qualities of a country walk, with the added thrill of successfully piecing together what happened when mining was active. In an age when there is more leisure time than ever, and a perceived need to exercise the mind as well as the body, mine walking is becoming deservedly popular.

Of course we are talking about mines abandoned for perhaps a century, where nature has had time to hide the worst scars. There's no pleasure in traipsing through a mine just closed, as one of the authors has at collieries in the past, with the buildings gutted and the ground crunchy with broken glass and roof slates: only sadness for the people who once worked there. Nor are mines which closed two centuries and more ago likely to yield much of interest short of an archaeological dig. It is those in between, dating from the time when Britain's engineering supremacy was unchallenged, that are the most likely to have left us with tangible, if at times baffling, ruins.

Sadly, many of Britain's traditional mining areas have little left to offer. Collieries, for example, have all but disappeared, save for a few early ones in an advanced state of decay. Shafts have been concreted, buildings swept away and waste tips reshaped and planted. Metal mines have fared rather better, being more remote from urban areas, though here too powerful destructive forces have been at work. To wind, rain and frost must be added rubbish tipping, vandalism, pillaging of stone and waste tips, highway and industrial building construction and so-called environmental improvement. This last usually means quite simply levelling and perhaps afforestation.

However for the interested there are still a few bright spots: Cornwall in particular. Here deep mining (1) is still with us - just - and pressure for redevelopment lower. Today's tourism industry is providing greater incentive to preserve the landscape. The buildings themselves were substantially constructed, especially those which held the great beam engines, where the house itself acted as the engine frame. More than 220 engine houses still survive in a fair state of completeness, despite having stood gutted and roofless for perhaps 100 years and more. Lesser ruins exist of 100 more. These "Cornish castles", their chimney stacks pointing like fingers to the heavens, act as beacons to the labyrinth of flooded shafts and levels beneath.

---

(1) By deep mining we mean mining by sinking shafts and driving levels as opposed to opencast mining, such as for china clay in the St Austell district. The latter is a flourishing modern industry. The only deep mine still at work is South Crofty, between Camborne and Redruth, but owing to the continuing low price of tin on world markets, its long-term future must be uncertain.

Dominant and meaningful as these structures are, they invite study of the less explicit relics of mining around them. They range from complete buildings to undulations or vestigial fragments of masonry hidden in undergrowth. This is where the interested observer needs guidance of the kind this book provides. At the time of writing only one tour operator provides guided car-borne trips to selected mining districts **(2)**. This book is for people who prefer to visit the mines by themselves.

A problem which struck an earlier attempt to produce a book of this kind now seems to have receded. This was when bulldozers moved in on one of the prime sites selected for coverage. But in the last few years there has been an astonishing turnaround. From a starting point of listing or scheduling structures as historic buildings to prevent demolition, some authorities are now finding the cash to carry out repairs. This is not a moment too soon, with some engine houses showing signs of collapse and bricks gone from many chimney tops.

By far the most ambitious scheme of this kind covers the Camborne-Redruth mining district and is called the Mineral Tramways Project **(3)**. Under it some 70 engine houses and other buildings are being stabilised as ruins (it stops short of total restoration) along with improving and restoring a network of tracks and bridleways. These include the routes of early railways and tramways over which ore was conveyed from, and coal, timber and other supplies brought into, the mines. The superb mining landscape which exists in this area will thus be preserved and it is possible that World Heritage status will be conferred. At present the project is in its infancy as finance from various sources - local authorities, private industry, Government in the form of Derelict Land Grants and English Heritage - has to be negotiated in easy stages.

It is not all good news, however. Shafts, instead of being traditionally walled or fenced, are being plugged with concrete and in most cases totally obscured except for a small marker **(4)**. Excavating for these plugs is enormously destructive of mine remains around the shafts. Contaminated land is another bogey. Onerous standards set by Brussels are resulting in topsoil tipping which in time will drastically alter the types of vegetation

---

(2) Cornwall of Mine Limited, whose parties are booked through Wheal Martyn China Clay Museum (phone 0726-850362).

(3) The project is being managed by Groundwork Kerrier in association with British Telecom, the Countryside Commission, Cornwall County Council, Kerrier and Carrick District Councils and local town and parish councils. From Easter 1995 a Mineral Tramways Project interpretation centre will be open to the public at Groundwork Kerrier's offices: Old Cowlin's Mill, Penhallick, Carn Brea, Redruth TR15 3AY (phone 0209-61297/8/9).

(4) A few selected shafts are being kept open where bats are known to nest, resulting in an ugly grilled structure built over the shaft. Others are being kept accessible by recognised mining groups by incorporating a locked trapdoor in the concrete cap, or by using a steel grille so that the shaft mouth remains visible.

growth which have for long been associated with mined areas. All this is happening despite opposition from naturalists, environmentalists, mining historians and even Cornwall County Council's own archaeologists **(5)**. It all comes under the heading of "managing" the mining landscape.

The whole question of doing landscaping work on Cornwall's old mine sites is a contentious one. Buildings apart, the risk of ending up with mine sites that no longer look like mine sites is greater than ever. So, if you prefer to enjoy the ruins before the new policies take full effect, now is the time!

Safety is paramount!

In describing what there is to see on mine sites traversed by the six walks in this book, it is not intended to provide a treatise on mining machinery. Underground operations are also outside the scope of this book, as are the social implications - the tough working conditions and social deprivation associated with Cornish mining in the past. For those wishing to pursue these subjects we give a list of further reading titles at the end.

By the judicious use of footnotes and a glossary to explain the technical terms used, we have been at pains to keep the text itself simple so that it can be readily comprehended during short pauses in the walk. We must stress, however, that mine sites can be dangerous. The reader is advised to stick to the routes recommended and abide by warnings of specifically risky areas, given in bold type. The risks are increased in strong winds or heavy rain or mist which can inhibit awareness of one's surroundings. Mine sites in general are not suitable places for young children, or the disabled.

It must also be borne in mind that construction or landscaping work on mine sites can occur anywhere. Changes to mine tracks, shaft protection and even the security of chimney stacks and old building walls due to freak weather could well occur between writing these words and publication. The publishers cannot take any responsibility for such changes, or for alteration or obliteration affecting features described.

Site interpretation

The more common types of structure and ground features associated with Cornish mining are described below. It is recommended that these notes are read before attempting any of the walks as they will make the site descriptions clearer. (Italicised words and phrases are included in the glossary.)

1. STRUCTURES

Pumping-engine house The houses for Cornish beam pumping engines tend to be the biggest surviving on any site owing to the large size of the

---

(5) The Cornwall Archaeological Unit, based at County Hall, Truro, has done much good work in recording and reporting on the ruins surviving on the principal mine sites. It also performs a watching rôle whenever deep excavation on a sensitive site is taking place.

The arrangement of a Cornish pumping engine as depicted in the Perran Foundry catalogue. The engine is Taylor's famous 85-inch on United Mines.
(Courtesy Trevithick Society)

engines needed, particularly on the inland mines which were inclined to be very wet. Cylinder diameters ranged up to 100 inches and piston strokes up to 11 feet. **(6)** Pumping houses are readily identifiable by a shaft (or indication of one) immediately in front of the thickest wall (the *bob wall*). The rocking beam was perched on this wall with the "outdoors" half of it protruding out over the shaft. The "indoors" end was linked to the piston in a large upright cylinder bolted down inside the house. A timber pump rod extending all the way down to the *sump* at the bottom of the shaft had its upper end attached to the beam. The *plunger pumps* attached to the pump rod at vertical intervals of 200 to 300 feet delivered water into the *rising main* on the down stroke of the rod, owing to the weight of the assembly. Each pump assembly was known as a *lift*. Steam acting on the engine piston then pushed it down, raising the pump rod ready for the next pumping stroke. **(7)** Water expelled from the rising main was delivered either into the *adit* or to surface or both. (A good supply was always needed at surface for *ore dressing*.)

It follows that the cylinder had to be very securely anchored down, and the massive masonry foundation or *loading* to which it was bolted may still be

---

(6) A pumping engine dating from 1892 with a 90-inch diameter cylinder is preserved static by the National Trust at East Pool, between Camborne and Redruth, and may be viewed between Easter and the end of October each year.

(7) The steam, or indoor, stroke usually took about 2 seconds, and the outdoor, pumping stroke 4-5 seconds, with pauses in between. This gave an engine the appearance of being guided by an unseen human hand. The normal speed for a large engine was 4-6 strokes per minute; it could be increased in wet weather but was always a most impressive sight. Writing in 1927 the late Dr Hamilton Jenkin expressed it thus: ".... the massive Cornish pumping engines whose beams, protruding above the shafts, alternately rise skyward and slowly sink again as they force up the water from the subterranean world beneath. Standing by one and watching the pump rod slowly rise and fall in the black abyss of the shaft, many people have realised for the first time what the call of mining means ...." Unfortunately it is no longer possible to see a Cornish pumping engine under steam in its native land, but some fine examples with cylinder diameters up to 90 inches may be seen working at London's Kew Bridge Steam Museum, and two smaller examples on selected weekends at Crofton canal pumping station near Great Bedwyn, Wiltshire. (For information on both, phone Kew Bridge on 081 568 4757.)

seen in almost every house. Sometimes the thick granite *bedstone* on which it stood remains visible, revealing the bolt pattern - from 4 to 6 according to the cylinder diameter. At the rear is the large *cylinder doorway* through which the beam and cylinder were brought into the house. In front of the loading is a deep pit, the *cockpit* or *cataract chamber* in which some of the engine's controls were situated. A low-level aperture in the bob wall took the exhaust, or eduction, pipe which passed across the cockpit to the condenser. This was usually placed outside, between the bob wall and the shaft, the condensate being returned to the boiler(s).

The boiler house consisted of a low annexe on one side of the engine house, at lower level and wide enough to take between one and six cylindrical *Cornish boilers.* The chimney stack is sometimes attached to the house and sometimes freestanding. It normally has a brick upper portion, architecturally featured, to suit a wall thickness which reduces towards the top.

On the edge of the shaft may be seen some masonry of a *balance pit.* This was to accommodate a *balance bob* to help counteract the weight of the pump rod. Some engines pumped from more than one shaft by using *flat-rod* drive to an *angle bob* at the remote shaft(s). Flat-rods reciprocated to and fro taking their motion from a *kingpost* on the balance bob. The angle bob changed this motion from horizontal to vertical in the shaft and were usually situated in a masonry pit. Flat-rods were supported on pendulum stands or rollers. They have left little evidence today except where they were entrenched. (Walk 3, Tywarnhayle *qv*.) Fragments of masonry from a pit for an angle bob still, however, cling to the edge of a few shafts.

Winding or *whim* engine houses are similar to pumping-engine houses but smaller: maximum cylinder diameter was 36 inches. They are readily distinguishable by having a masonry loading for the *crankshaft* in front with a deep slot for a single large *flywheel.* **(8)** Sometimes the bob wall was recessed to accommodate it. Arrangement of the engine in the house was similar to a pumping engine but it was usual to work it double acting, that is, steam was applied alternately to both top and bottom of the piston. Since the crankshaft, with winding drum or *cage* attached, revolved smoothly there were no pauses between strokes. Beam whims were normally aligned with the shaft from which they hoisted, one or two ropes being led out from the cage and over pulley wheels, or *poppet heads,* carried on a *headgear* above the shaft. A few steam whims had the winding cage on an upright axle driven from the crankshaft by a bevel gear. In this case the engine did not have to be aligned with a shaft, and several could be served. Some smaller whims were all-enclosed in the house instead of being half outdoors. **(9)**

(8) A beam whim with a 30-inch diameter cylinder and the last one built, in 1887, is also preserved at East Pool and operated non-authentically by a concealed electric drive.
(9) Such an example dating from 1840 is preserved by the National Trust at Levant (near Botallack) and is steamed during the summer season.

Steam whims were generally used only on the deeper shafts, a *horse whim* being otherwise employed. Except for an occasional circular *whim plat,* these have mostly disappeared without trace. Before the turn of the century beam whims began to be displaced by horizontal whims, that is the cylinder (or pair of cylinders) lay horizontally on a masonry or concrete beds usually made long enough to carry the *drum shaft* as well. Such engines were enclosed in a simple brick or masonry house or sometimes a mere timber or sheet-clad shed. Since they took steam at a higher pressure than beam engines they usually puffed their exhaust to atmosphere instead of condensing. **(10)**

For centuries, hoisting in Cornish mines was only of rock, using a *kibble* or a *skip:* miners had to use ladders. A device called a *man engine* was used in a few very deep mines from 1846 but serious hoisting of men using a steam whim fitted with a *gig* had to wait until later in the century. Another form of hoisting was by *capstan* for handling pump rods and other equipment in an *engine shaft.* This was a slow and heavy job, being done using a manual capstan, of which very few traces survive, and later by low-geared steam engine. A few capstans consisted of a winding drum geared to the crankshaft of a beam whim. (Walk 4, Lyle's whim, *qv.*)

In a small mine a steam whim could be used both to hoist and to pump from a shaft. A short run of flat-rods to the shaft was then worked by a pumping crank geared down from the crankshaft. It was not unknown for a single beam engine to pump, hoist and drive stamps or a crusher, using clutches, when a mine was in its infancy.

Stamps and crusher engine house Driving *Cornish* (tin) *stamps,* in order to reduce the rock containing the ore to a fine sand, was commonly done by a beam engine similar to a whim but having two flywheels. Maximum cylinder size generally was 40 inches. Unfortunately, none has been preserved. The stamps themselves, of the gravity type, were lifted by a long camshaft *(stamps axle)* driven from the crankshaft through a ratchet device which allowed the engine to run backwards to warm up and generate a vacuum in the condenser before starting. Today ground undulations are often the only sign of where stamps stood. Stamps engines commonly had the boiler house at the rear to allow room for attaching stamps to both ends of the crankshaft. Only 1% or at best 2% of the mineral vein or lode consisted of the cassiterite or tin oxide required for the smelter, hence the large amount of work which had to be done to the ore to obtain a saleable product.

Wheelpit Water was the chief source of motive power on Cornish mines

---

(10) The majority of horizontal whim engines used in Cornwall in recent times were built by Holman Brothers of Camborne, whose twin-cylinder drop-valve engines were extremely successful. Sadly none have been preserved but a small example of a Holman twin-drum winder, originally installed new at King Edward Mine in about 1906, can be seen at the Poldark Mine near Helston.

before steam engines were invented. Even afterwards, extensive use was made of waterwheels where a sufficient natural flow of water was available, because coal in Cornwall was expensive, usually coming from South Wales. Wheels ranging from a few feet to 60 feet in diameter could be used to perform any of the functions described above, though in large mines their use was mainly confined to ore dressing. **(11)** Larger examples were normally mounted in a wheelpit, a masonry boxlike structure enclosing the bottom half of the wheel with the side walls carrying the wheel bearings. Such pits could be sunk in the ground or built on the surface (Walk 6 , Boswedden *qv)*. Few large examples survive in Cornwall: either the masonry has been robbed or they have been filled in for safety.

Calciner Another small ruin is that of a *calciner,* often used from the 1880s to recover arsenic as a by-product **(12)**. Its function was to roast the ore and pass the gases through a labyrinth or long flue, wherein the arsenic condensed and formed crystals adhering to the interior. This led to a chimney or "arsenic stack". Traces of the circular rotating grate can be seen in some ruined examples of *Brunton calciners,* also of the labyrinth and the chambers via which the crystals were extracted, and the arsenic stack.

Compressor house Rockdrills driven by compressed air began replacing hand drills from about 1870, but only gradually, because the problems of their bulk and production of killer dust took time to solve. Steam-driven air compressors on surface were small to begin with and could be placed in a boiler-house annexe. From the 1890s, however, large *two-stage* air compressors, with either horizontal or vertical cylinders, began to be erected, requiring sizable engine beds, a masonry or brick house, and a boiler house and stack. The ruins of several survive.

Mill buildings Tin ore mixed with water, known as the *pulp,* had to undergo a number of different sluicing processes in order to "concentrate" it, that is get rid of the abundance of unwanted rock. The work was normally carried out by men, women and even children in wooden sheds which have long since disappeared. Late last century Cornish stamps began to be replaced by *Californian stamps,* and more recently by ball mills and cone crushers. With these more modern plants the whole process was enclosed in a wooden or sheet-clad building known as the *mill.* A handful

---

(11) When a waterwheel was used for pumping flatrod drive was employed, the rods sometimes extending for half a mile to the mine shaft. For hoisting, the cage was clutched to the drive shaft, the kibble or skip returning by gravity. A stamps axle or crusher was usually driven through gearing. Dry weather causing a temporary water shortage was the usual bugbear of companies relying on water power: it could bring the mine to a halt. So could a severe frost. Some mines therefore kept steam engines as a standby, or to augment the power from a wheel.
(12) In earlier times, if necessary the ore was roasted in a burning house and the fumes were allowed to escape through a tall stack, simply to get rid of the arsenic, along with sulphides of copper and iron. This practice was not popular with local farmers!

of these structures are still complete though ruinous **(13)**, but the concrete foundations of the plant they contained still exist on a number of sites (Walk 2, Wheal Kitty *qv)*. In a brief intermediate period early this century batteries of *Frue vanners* - later replaced by *shaking tables* - were employed to concentrate the tin ore crushed by the stamps. Good examples of the long, low vanner houses built for these are visible on Walk 4 (Basset Mines).

Each generation of ore treatment plant had two things in common. They were arranged on downhill slopes, and the *washwater* which conveyed the pulp from one process to the next ended up in the nearest river or stream, or the sea. These *tailings* always carried a low fraction of cassiterite - hence the creation of the *tin-streaming* industry.

Count house and headquarters buildings Many mines had a pretentious office or *count house* which often doubled as the mine captain's residence **(14)**. Lesser buildings usually erected close by included smithy, fitting shop, carpenters' shop, stables and *miners' dry.* Often the buildings were arranged in a courtyard with a surrounding wall and gate for security. (Open or covered coal stores for the engines were similarly provided.) Today a large number of count houses survive as residences though the other buildings have mostly gone or been drastically rebuilt. Of the few survivors, most have been retained for farm purposes.

2. GROUND FEATURES

Waste dumps or *burrows* Most mines have left some disturbance of the ground as evidence, ranging from small overgrown mounds of material raised from long-forgotten shafts to massive heaps of spoil on which little or nothing will grow - at least, not for many years. Very few of the latter now remain undisturbed: they have been robbed for road building, re-treated for ore they might still contain or simply levelled on the pretext of environmental improvement. The 1970s and mid-1980s when the tin price rose to almost £10,000 a ton saw a peak in re-treating for tin. Other materials discarded when mining was active have been sought at different times, for example the search for wolfram to obtain tungsten for the aircraft and armament industries during World War 2.

Shafts and adits The mouths of these are mostly no longer open. The time-honoured way of marking the shaft of an abandoned mine was to build a low circular stone wall around, known as a stone hedge. The shaft itself would either be left open or covered with timber planks and turf, leaving it to future generations to decide what to do when the timber rotted! As shafts are filled and capped in today's safety-conscious climate,

---

(13) South Crofty mine still has its own mill but currently sends all its ore to the more up-to-date mill at Wheal Jane which uses a flotation process. The latter achieves an 86% tin oxide recovery, which is very high, the rest being lost in the tailings. The Wheal Jane mill is also capable of recovering by-products including zinc, copper and arsenic.

(14) It used to be said that if a mine proved uneconomic, as in Cornwall most did, then at least the count house would be worth something on the property market!

fewer of the old stone hedges may be seen, though in one area **(15)** they have recently been built or rebuilt.

Adit mouths have very largely collapsed owing to the unsupported weathered rock of the portal, but some still show themselves as ochre-stained water oozing from the ground **(16)**.

Leats (watercourses)   To divert a supply of water to a mine for waterwheels and/or ore dressing, miners constructed leats following the contours from a river or stream upstream of the mine. Remnants of these can be seen in many places, though the earthworks were kept simple.

Storage and cooling ponds To store water delivered from a leat against drought, mines would construct one or more ponds on a convenient piece of level ground. Some ponds were used solely to cool the condensing water for one or more engines. Rising vapour from an engine cooling pond on a chilly winter's evening was one of the sights of Cornwall in earlier times! Fine tailings from ore dressing were often used to keep ponds watertight, clay being scarce in many parts of Cornwall. Today changes in vegetation growth can mark the sites of ponds though again, landscaping is gradually destroying them.

Open pits Owing to the depth of the richer deposits, large-scale opencast mining was not often used in Cornwall's metal mines **(17)**. Smaller pits and depressions where *lode back working* was employed can still be seen in places, notably on Walk 6 at Boswedden Mine, but larger pits are under threat for refuse disposal, which after topsoiling and landscaping leaves no trace.

Railways and *tramways* Apart from the trackbeds of early railways or plateways which served the mines, most mines had their own internal tramways for shifting rock from the shafts to the stamps or waste tips. These were man- or horse-powered, occasionally steam **(18)**. In places earthworks are still visible but elevated construction on a timber trestle was widely employed, leaving little trace today.

---

(15) The Poldice Valley Trust, near St Day, have deliberately set out to preserve the mining landscape on the site of the old Poldice tin- and copper-mine. See *The Landfall Book of the Poldice Valley* (1990).

(16) A few adits which are still open are being gated to permit access by responsible bodies.

(17) A notable exception was the Great Perran Iron Lode, between Newquay and Perranporth, where mechanical excavators were used up until the 1940s. China clay mining in the St Austell district is, of course, a totally different operation involving hydraulic mining techniques carried out in huge open pits.

(18) Dolcoath mine employed tramway gauge of 1ft 10 in and two steam locomotives. Basset Mines used approximately 2 ft and a single German-built steam locomotive (Walks 5 and 4 *qv*).

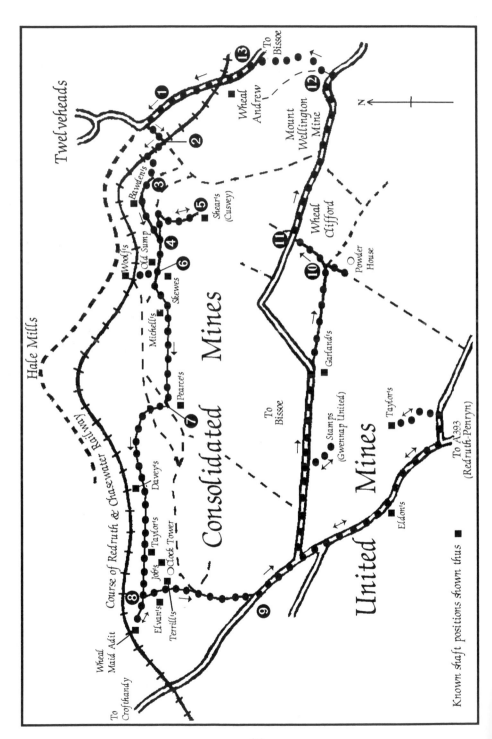

1
CONSOLIDATED & UNITED MINES

This tour involves a walk of about three miles, plus several short optional extensions which would add perhaps a little over another mile in total. Most of the first half of the route runs along the southern side of a valley which has been so intensively mined, as well as having been put to other industrial uses, that it will probably always be "derelict land". A few areas support little if any plant growth, but heather and gorse have colonised most of the slopes, and a surprisingly wide range of trees, shrubs and other plants lend variety to the scene, many of them probably a happy by-product of the dumping of garden rubbish. The latter part of the walk is mostly along minor roads and lanes or tracks in the rather windswept area known as United Downs. The region covered by the walk is one of immense importance in the history of copper mining, and although the remains on surface may be at first sight less striking than those on most of the other sites dealt with in this book, there is in fact a wealth of fascinating, if sometimes enigmatic, evidence still there if you know where to look. The engine houses include at least two that are probably among the oldest surviving in Cornwall, and at the other end of the time scale there are relics to be seen of mining enterprises dating back less then twenty years. An important mineral railway served these mines, and parts of the route described follow sections of its main line and at least one of its branches.

LOCATION: About 5 miles south west of Truro and a mile east of St Day. The area explored lies between the villages of Twelveheads and Carharrack. Grid reference for starting point: SW 761 420. OS maps: Pathfinder (1:25,000): No. 1360 (Truro). Landranger (1:50,000): No. 204 (Truro, Falmouth & surrounding area).

HOW TO GET THERE By car: From Truro, take the A39 south towards Falmouth. After about four miles, a little way after passing the first turning into Devoran, take the minor road on the right, to Bissoe. (The first mile-or-so of this road follows what was the course of the Redruth and Chasewater Railway.) Continue ahead up the valley, passing under the viaduct carrying the Truro-Falmouth branch line. Ignore all side turnings until you have passed through Bissoe and crossed the bridge over the Carnon River at Point Mills. A few yards beyond that there is a filling station on the left; take the right turning opposite, signposted to Mount Wellington Mine. Ignore the left turning later. After a little over half a mile you will be close to Twelveheads, and can park in one of the laybys beside the road - preferably the largest one, on the right a few yards before the Twelveheads village sign. (To give directions from Redruth and elsewhere would be impracticable in a portable book! Suffice to say that your best plan is to make for Carharrack and use your map to get you from there to the valley road on the south side of Twelveheads.)

By public transport: Western National bus service 94 links Truro with Twelveheads (not Sundays). See current timetable.

CONSOLIDATED AND UNITED MINES
(with a brief outline of later mining ventures in the same area)

The small district stretching roughly from Carharrack to Twelveheads has been intensively mined for a very long time, and during the second half of the 18th century at least a dozen mines here proved very rich in copper. By about 1780 one group (Wheals Virgin, East and West Virgin, Girl, Maid, Fortune and Cusvey; Collins also mentions "the old Carharrack", Wheal Lovelace, Deebles and Wheal Wentworth) had amalgamated as Great Consolidated Mines, and another including Wheals Andrew, Clifford, Cupboard, Poldory, Squire and Ale and Cakes had become United Mines. In 1787 the novelist William Beckford visited "Consols", as that group soon came to be called (with the stress on the second syllable), and wrote this description. "At every step one stumbles upon ladders that lead into utter darkness or funnels that exhale warm copperous vapours. All around these openings the ore is piled up in heaps ready for purchasers. I saw it drawn reeking out of the mine by the help of a machine called a whim put in motion by mules, which in their turn are stimulated by impish children hanging over the poor brutes and flogging them without respite. The dismal scene of whims, suffering mules and hillocks of cinders, extends for miles. Huge iron engines creaking and groaning invented by Watt and tall chimneys smoking and flaming, that seem to belong to Old Nicholas's abode, diversify the prospect." Beckford contrasted the mine officials who "regale upon beef, pudding and brandy" with the miners, "woeful figures in tattered garments with pickaxes on their shoulders" who "crawled out of a dark fissure and repaired to a hovel, which I learnt was a gin-shop." Towards the end of the century, competition from Anglesey threatened the rations of beef, pudding and brandy, and both Consols and United were closed in about 1805. In 1811, when Consols was described as "totally abandoned", United was restarted, and within a year or two Michael and John Williams of Scorrier were manager and purser. Soon after that, John Williams tried to form a company to reopen Consols, but in the event it was the Norwich-born John Taylor, armed with £65,000 supplied by his London shareholders, who succeeded in getting that group working again, in 1819. The gamble paid off handsomely, and from 1823 to 1840 Consols' annual output of copper outstripped all its rivals, even Dolcoath. In 1839 Taylor took over United, and by 1830 the employees numbered over 3,000. In 1839, as a result of opposition from the Williams family and their associates, Taylor's application to renew the lease of Consols was refused, and his response was to "pick out the eyes" of the mine, that is, he stripped it of all available ore including underground stockpiles, and sold in that year the extraordinary total of 23,194 tons. From then on the annual output fell steadily. In 1843 Consols' figures were overtaken by those of United. In 1857 United annexed Consols, forming a new group named Clifford Amalgamated. Its output during the 1860s was still huge, but the great days of Cornish copper mining were over. When the mine closed in 1869 it had over 80 miles of underground workings and 18 engine houses ("the greatest number of engines used on any Cornish mine" according to D.B.Barton); nearly a million tons of copper, plus some tin and other metals, had been sold, with a total value of some £6m in contemporary terms - almost impossible to translate into modern values, but clearly a staggering figure. 1870 was not quite the end of the story, of course: between about 1900 and 1909 the dumps were reworked for tin by a company named Gwennap United, but the techniques employed, though the most up-to-date available at the time, were inadequate to make a financial success of the venture. Finally - or at least we presume that adverb will prove to be accurate - during the decade from the mid 1970s to the mid '80s Mount Wellington mined parts of the Consols and United setts for tin.   One problem that had always beset Consols was very high temperatures at deep levels *. Another was that it was an unusually wet mine - hence, of course, the large number of big pumping engines employed by Consols in its heyday - and the water was an important reason for the early demise of Mount Wellington.

* A huge and beautiful section plan of Clifford Amalgamated and Consolidated United mine, held at the Cornwall County Record Office, includes the comment:

"The temperature of the deep Levels in this Mine is remarkable:-
At 220 fathoms the Water is 110°, the Air 100°.
At 230 fathoms the Water is 124°, the Air 120°."

1 *If you parked in one of the laybys mentioned above, start the walk by continuing up the valley road, and turn up the track on the left immediately before the road curves right into Twelveheads.* After 100 yards a fairly narrow, level track crosses the one you're on: this marks the course of the Redruth and Chasewater Railway. Up on the left is Mount Wellington Mine.

2 *Turn right along the railway in a shallow cutting - it had just been cleared when we were there but is likely to be rather muddy. After about 150 yards - just after the fields on each side give way to heather and scrub - a smaller path crosses the railway track. Turn left on this, up a steep slope, and almost immediately bear right, diagonally up the slope, along what is little more than an animal track.*

Soon you will see the remains of dry stone retaining walls in front of you on two levels. Just what went on in this area is a bit of a mystery! The ground contours suggest a discharge point for copper ore into wagons. Faint traces of an arsenic flue running up the hill from the lower level almost certainly indicate the site of a burning house for roasting off the arsenic, in the days before arsenic recovery had become established practice. The clinker present at the west end of this site could be from the burning house, or spillage from the boiler house of Bawden's engine at a higher level, which will be seen shortly.

Now follow the flue up the slope until it peters out and one reaches a broad track.

3 *Turn right along it.*

Very soon a large fenced area appears below the track on the right: the site of Bawden's Shaft of Wheal Fortune **(1)**. This is one of several big pumping shafts on Consols with a narrower winding shaft beside it: a common fence surrounds both. A few yards to the west is what looks like the site of a circular capstan plat, with a retaining wall below its edge to protect what was possibly a branch of the Redruth and Chasewater Railway over which ore was taken away.

Return to the track and continue westwards. Soon you will reach a mound built up to deter New Age travellers, but before crossing it .....

4 *..... turn sharp left up a steep joining track for an optional detour to Cusvey Mine. After a short distance turn sharp right up a less steep track.*

It gives you a good bird's-eye view of Twelveheads, the most prominent buildings being the chapel and the restored watermill further left. (The valley situation of the village made it a good site for water-powered stamps - hence its name. Small sets of stamps commonly had twelve "heads", the heavy wooden or iron rods which were lifted and dropped to crush the tin ore.) Beside the junction of the tracks a high bank seems to have served a dual purpose. First, it retained a large mine pond, or reservoir, to store water for engine and ore-dressing purposes. Second, masonry fragments indicate the course of an arsenic flue. Both pond and flue are clearly visible from further up the track.

Keep to the main path as it curves anticlockwise uphill and soon brings you to the two engine houses at Shear's Shaft, Cusvey Mine **(2)**, with the slightly banana-shaped chimney stack between them. ("Cusvey", otherwise "Cusvean", derives from the Cornish for "small wood". The word is usually pronounced "<u>Cuz</u>-vee", but a knowledgeable gentleman from St Day insists

---

(1) The engine here was a 90-inch which stood on the east side of the shaft. The beam whim engine stood some distance to the west - a few small trees mark the site - and there is evidence that the mine's horse-drawn tramway system, which was linked with the Redruth and Chasewater line, had a branch leading to the shaft from the west.

(2) Here the most important feature is the age of the structures. The larger, more accessible and less overgrown house of the pumping engine could date from 1826, making it the oldest in Cornwall. The shaft in front is boarded - a relic of the recent operations of Wheal Jane, about a mile away to the north-east, whose management carried out explorations in this area. The first pumping engine in the house was a 70-inch, but after a few years it - or perhaps just the cylinder - was replaced by one of 65 inches. Note particularly the fine dressed stone arch above the "plug doorway" which overlooks the shaft. There was a similarly fine arch over the large "cylinder doorway" at the rear before it collapsed. Some of these early engines had wooden "weighposts" carrying the valve gear, which were anchored at first floor level to a massive timber beam to provide rigidity. This beam probably accounts for the unusual square openings in the wing walls each side above the driver's position.

The whim, or hoisting, shaft is separate from the pumping shaft - a practice common to several of the principal shafts of these mines - and is slightly to the east. It and the whim-engine house aligned with it were totally overgrown when we were last there in late autumn 1993, and inaccessible without cutting gear. The whim was totally enclosed in its house.

Shear's Shaft, Cusvey Mine: beam whim (left of chimney) and 65 inch engine house, 1st January 1987

The same buildings as seen from the north side, 1990

it is properly "C'z-<u>vay</u>".) On the left side of the path as you approach the buildings is more evidence of the arsenic flue; then it appears as an opening in the ground on the right, heading towards the chimney stack. It therefore seems that the stack, which is of substantial diameter, not only served the boilers of the two engines here but also discharged the burnt-off arsenic fumes to atmosphere. It is possible that this flue and the one leading from the burning-house site we saw earlier are one and the same: there is no evidence of an arsenic stack lower down the slope. Arsenic flues of this length, some 250 yd, were by no means uncommon in Cornwall in order to discharge the fumes well above the nearby farmland.

The first engine house reached is that of the pumping engine, which bears striking detail similarities to that of Taylor's (Consols) engine, seen later in this tour. In front of the house the shaft is protected by thick boarding. If the light is good, this affords a glimpse of the shaft itself, which underlies gently to the east.

5 *To continue the walk, return the same way, downhill to the mound over the track, and cross it, heading west:* in clear weather you will see St Day ahead, dominated by its church and clock tower.

Soon a ditch across the track, also to deter New Age travellers, heralds an area of trees and bushes on the left. That there has been machinery here is suggested by a long, masonry-lined trench in the ground, possibly a boiler mounting, and a fragment of small-section winding rope. A possible explanation is that a steam hoist was erected here long after the mine's closure to conduct underground exploration.

The nearest shafts are a pair on the opposite side of the track a few yards further on, called Old Sump. Here the right-hand one appears to have been the pumping shaft and the smaller one for hoisting, but nothing definite is known about the machinery employed. There is faint evidence of an engine house beneath the present track, and it is supposed that one of the Watt engines on Wheal Fortune stood here in earlier times.

6 *Immediately beyond the shafts, we suggest another detour down the fairly steep, roughish path on the right, which cuts back a little* and brings you down to another large shaft (Woolf's, at 300 fathoms one of the deepest on Consols), surrounded by a wire fence. On the valley side of the shaft are the scanty remains of the house built in 1826 for the 90" pumping engine **(3)**. The mound of apparently black soil with a tree growing on it is actually a heap of ashes and cinders generated by the engine's five boilers! The whim shaft here, adjoining the engine shaft on the west, has been capped off and obscured in recent years.

The level track running beside the shaft was the course of the Redruth and Chasewater Railway: there is at least one displaced granite "sett" or sleeper block quite close to the old shaft. Looking back towards Twelveheads you will see a widened section where there was a short loop; according to Barton this was used for storage of wagons, but it was probably a

---

(3) Woolf's Shaft took its name from the designer of the 90-inch pumping engine installed there, Arthur Woolf. It was obtained secondhand in 1826 from Wheal Alfred (Gwinear), where it had come out best in a trial against one of Woolf's compound engines.

Bawden's Shaft, part of Wheal Fortune.
The site of the 90-inch engine is in the foreground.

The ruins of Taylor's 85-inch pumping-engine house and stack at Consols,
with tailings lagoons in the background, 29th January 1989

Kenneth inspecting a row of granite setts, part of the Wheal Fortune branch of the Redruth & Chasewater Railway, February 1994

loading/unloading point also. In the opposite direction, towards Hale Mills, the route of the line as it passes through the deepest of its cuttings is rather overgrown. Here it is possible to appreciate the clever engineering of the line, which maintains a fairly steady gradient all the way up to its summit on the slopes of Carn Marth.

Return up the track you have just descended, to the point where you left it close to Old Sump Shaft, and turn right. From here you can see the group of cottages down in the valley at Hale Mills; just above them is the cutting made for the railway's branch line to Poldice Mine, which was originally intended to continue as far as Wheal Busy near Chacewater. The shafts to the left of the cutting, with prominent waste heaps, belonged to Wheal Maid. A good deal further right, on the eastern slope of what has come to be known as the Poldice Valley, is the small, ivy-shrouded stack of possibly the oldest surviving engine house in Cornwall, Wheal Henry **(4)**.

Now continue westwards, not along the level track but up the inclined one which leads off to the left. Above you, what appears to be a tunnel leads directly into the waste tip beside Skewes Shaft. The track soon levels out and after a short distance you see on your right an open shaft with a large steel mesh cap. This is Michell's Shaft, and on the left side of the track, just south-east of the shaft, can be seen where a cutting was formed for a horsewhim circle for hoisting.

A few yards beyond the shaft another trench has been cut across the track to keep wheeled vehicles at bay. Mounds and trenches have become a feature of Consols since the mass exodus of New Age travellers in May 1994. In the same area, close inspection reveals a few granite setts partly obscured on the left side of the track. The two bolt holes betray them to have been railway sleepers: a clue that this faintly rising track was another part of the mineral railway. Not much further along you will find a splendid group of exposed sleeper setts still in place - at least thirty of them. This was, in fact, one of the two branch lines which diverged from the main one at the Great Yard, just this side of Carharrack. One went south to serve United Mines, and the other - this one - ran more-or-less parallel with the main line, but at a higher level, along the full length of Consols, ending at Wheal Fortune. The wagons on these branch lines were always horse-drawn. **(5)** A short way beyond the setts you will reach the large fenced shaft (currently used as a rubbish dump) known as Pearce's **(6)**,

---

(4) Site interpretation suggests that it contained a Watt-type engine of around 1800, that is 16 years before the first true Cornish engine at Dolcoath Mine went to work.

(5) Reliable information about the routes adopted for the branch lines is hard to come by: it has been stated, for example, that there were actually two branches for Consols, one at high level serving Pearce's Shaft and another lower down, to Wheal Fortune. The difficulty for the modern historian is compounded by the fact that the contours of the landscape itself seem in some places to have been subject to quite drastic changes over the years. The fact of the matter may be that the lines were relocated according to the varying needs of the mine at different periods.

(6) Another of the principal engine shafts of the mine, this one had a 65-inch engine. Traces of its engine house may be found under the *cotoneaster horizontalis* spreading over the western edge of the shaft: indeed, this plant occurs all over this area, and is an excellent pointer to the presence of crumbling masonry!

which stands a little way to the left. Here again there are two shafts, for hoisting and pumping.

7 *From Pearce's Shaft, walk down the slope towards the dams in the valley bottom,* built in order to create a tailings reservoir for Billiton Minerals, who in the 1970s tried dredging for tin in the mud of the Carnon River. Later Carnon Consolidated took it over and have planning permission to use it for dumping the concentrate of tailings from their "new" South Crofty dressing mill. This of course has never been built, and the South Crofty ore is still processed at Wheal Jane. Parts of the enormously expensive plastics pumping main have been reclaimed, but portions remain in situ, some of them still full of "slurry".

Just before reaching a wire fence, turn left, heading towards distant St Day once more. The huge mounds of mine waste on the south side of the track are of recent origin, from Wheal Jane, and have drastically altered the ground contours in this area.

Soon you will pass the scanty remains, on your left, of Davey's whim-engine house. *A few yards beyond that, a very short diversion to the slightly lower level on the right* will bring you to the fenced shafts, beside which until quite recent years stood a historic pumping-engine house **(7)**, demolished in order to make way for a roadway which seems, in the event, to have been very little used. The base of the bob wall can still be seen beside the road on the south side of the shaft to the west: the one to the east was the whim shaft. The angled slot in the bob wall took the engine's eduction pipe to the condenser.

Return to the upper level and continue westwards as before. A short way down on the right can be seen one of the few surviving sections of the route of the main line of the mineral railway in this landscape which has been so mauled and pummelled. Beyond Davey's a particularly nasty trench has to be crossed. Further along, up on the left is an almost miraculous survivor, the very ruinous but still impressive 85-inch pumping-engine house at Taylor's Shaft **(8)**, and a little further away the scanty

---

(7) Davey's 80-inch pumping engine, installed in 1832, was a significant performer and became the "show" engine of the mine. Visitors would be taken to see her in preference to any of the others. She was built by the Copperhouse Foundry at Hayle and possibly incorporated the beam of one of Arthur Woolf's short-lived 2-cylinder compound engines. Her designer was Samuel Hocking who with Michael Loam succeeded Woolf as engineer to Consolidated Mines when the latter retired in 1830. Davey's engine had the distinction of being the subject of the first full published description of a Cornish pumping engine. This was in 1834 following a visit by the French mining engineer, Charles Combes. Davey's Shaft reached an eventual depth of 300 fm. A superb model of the 80-inch engine made by Frank Woodall is on display at Kew Bridge Steam Museum in West London.
(8) Taylor's takes its name from the mine's manager, John Taylor: see the note on the history of Consols and United. Again, the pumping shaft is the western one, with the adjacent whim shaft on the east. The similarity between this pumping-engine house and the one seen earlier at Cusvey is striking; like that, it is among the earliest surviving ones in Cornwall, having been built in 1827 for a 70-inch engine. She was recylindered to 85-inch in 1833, in an operation which took only three months, to increase her pumping capacity. Taylor's Shaft reached a depth of 250 fm before the mines closed. All three whim engines of which remains exist appear to have been all-enclosed in the house.

Frank Woodall's model of Davey's 80-inch pumping engine,
photographed at Kew. Note manual capstan and shearlegs over
the shaft for raising and lowering pitwork. (See Footnote (7).)

Davey's engine house as it was in about 1981.
The 80-inch engine here was the showpiece of Consols.

remains - little more than a chimney stack - of the associated whim-engine house. You can also glimpse, on higher ground, a much sturdier structure, the Consols clock tower **(9)**.

8 *When you reach a double line of rusty iron posts across the track, turn left, uphill.* (But first you might care to continue ahead for a short distance - downhill at first, but ignore the right fork down to the valley bottom. Continue ahead till your progress is halted by a chain-link fence on the edge of a sudden drop. Below you now, on the left, is the bricked-up mouth of the modern Wheal Maid Adit **(10)**. Beyond that, at the same level as you are standing, the course of the mineral railway is clear, as it heads towards the Crofthandy level crossing on its way to Carharrack and Redruth. Return the same way.)

The uphill track soon takes you past another fenced shaft on the right, much used for depositing rubbish. This appears from Dines to be Elvan's. A little further on, on higher ground, a large fence encloses what appear to be three shafts. On the southern edge of the most westerly one (Terrill's Shaft) is clear evidence of a large pumping engine - but what size it was and when it was erected the authors have been unable to discover! Somewhere just to the north, but now obscured, is Francis' Shaft, famous for an early shaft-sinking record **(11)**. The whole area, part of the Wheal Virgin section of Consols, is covered with cinders, presumably from the engine boilers. The easternmost shaft is also open beneath its Clwyd cap and bears traces of a possible angle-bob pit for pumping by a remotely situated engine to the east.

From here you can go over to the left for a closer look at Taylor's and the clock tower; but to continue the walk carry straight on past Terrill's Shaft and along the wide track that leads to the road, emerging opposite Tony Craze's scrap-metal yard. (The site of the stamps engine erected to deal with any tin found in depth is to the left of the track, about 50 yd from Francis' Shaft, but there is precious little evidence of it. As you continue, on the right side of this track are a few more granite setts, obviously part of one of the branch lines, probably the link between United and Consols. See footnote (5).)

9 *Turn left on the road.*

At this point you can if you wish make a short diversion to view Eldon's (or

---

(9) Its "works" were utilised for St Day's town clock after the Clifford Amalgamated closure in 1869: it continued showing the time there well into the present century.

(10) This was an exploratory tunnel driven by Wheal Jane, whose mineral rights extended over a wide area. It came to an abrupt halt with the tin price collapse in 1985 and all equipment has since been removed.

(11) A remarkable feature of Consols was its early adoption of the practice of excavating a shaft by rising and sinking simultaneously from several points underground as well as working from surface. The practice reached its climax in 1829 when, between March and December, a team of 100 men successfully excavated Francis' Shaft to a depth of 205 fm in just nine-and-a-half months. This record, achieved before the days of mechanical rockdrills, was probably never surpassed anywhere in the world. It is said that on being squared off, the various sections of the shaft lined up perfectly.

Garland's 80-inch engine house with Gwennap United stamps in the background. Both were occupied for burrow re-treatment early this century.

The round powder house (explosives store) at Wheal Clifford

Little) engine house and Taylor's Shaft (not to be confused with Taylor's Shaft on Consols). For this, *ignore the next left turning, and continue ahead towards the entrance to a large rubbish tip,* which now covers the main areas of United Mines.

Eldon's engine house **(12)** stands on the right side of the road immediately before the tip entrance. During the short-lived Gwennap United burrow-treating operation at the turn of the century the top was lopped off and it was converted to serve as an office. In recent years it has been stabilised by the local authority and bears a plaque to that effect. The shaft, now filled and capped, is at the south-east end of the house. Nearby was Hocking's 85-inch pumping engine, whose house survived until the 1950s. It used to stand just inside the tip entrance on the left side of the access road and was the last of United's large pumping-engine houses to survive.

To view Taylor's Shaft and the site of its famous 85-inch engine, *continue further along the road and bear left at the next road junction, about 150 yd beyond the tip entrance. A few yards past the junction is a small layby on the left, bordered by an earth bund or ramp. Take one of the tracks over the bund and follow a wide track away from the road for a few yards; turn left where another track joins, then follow it as it bears right, so that you are still walking away from the road, with a stock-car racing area on your left.* This is the Ale and Cakes section of United. Taylor's Shaft **(13)** is just over 100 yd from the road and is covered by a heavy metal grid. This is the pumping shaft where a splendid 85-inch engine stood, on the north side of the shaft; the whim shaft a few yards south-west of it has been obscured. Fragments of the engine house can be seen in its north-east corner, but for how long these pitiful remains will stay visible is anybody's guess.

The environs of the shaft afford an excellent front view of the Gwennap

(12) Eldon's or Little pumping engine had a 30-inch cylinder and was erected in the 1830s for the sole purpose of drawing cooling water to surface from the adit. Like the large pumping engines on the two mines it performed a high duty.

(13) Taylor's 85-inch engine on United Mines was built by the Perran Foundry in 1840 and erected by mine managers John Taylor & Sons on the Ale and Cakes section of the mine. For her first few years she was Cornwall's top performer in terms of duty (efficiency). In September/October 1842 she achieved 107 millions (lb of water lifted 1 ft high by the consumption of one bushel of coal), the highest duty ever recorded in *Lean's Engine Reporter.* The engine was designed by the engineering partnership of Hocking & Loam, with strokes of 11ft in the cylinder and 10 ft in the shaft. A splendid model with part of the engine house cut away to reveal the interior is on display in London's Science Museum. This reveals an unusual surface feature: the engine had twin iron balance boxes, one each side of the shaft. Until a recent shaft protection operation the two masonry mountings for them could still be seen. A reduced-size version of the well-known drawing of Taylor's engine that appeared in the Perran Foundry catalogue is on page 10 of this book.

When the celebrated engineering writer Dr William Pole saw the engine working in 1842 she was cutting off the steam after only one tenth of the stroke. Whilst in operational terms this helped the high duty, the rapid acceleration it induced at the beginning of the stroke put a great strain on the wooden pump-rod and pitwork in the shaft. After a few years and several serious breakages, including a bad smash with this particular engine, the use of such short cutoffs in Cornwall became frowned upon, and figures of between a third and a quarter were adopted. Preserved Cornish pumping engines working today at Crofton, Wiltshire, and Kew Bridge Steam Museum, West London, use a cutoff of about a half, safe operation being paramount.

Gwennap United stamps-engine house on United Mines,
installed 30 years after the mine's closure.

United 34-inch stamps engine house which stands on raised ground to the north-west [see footnote (14)], but we cannot recommend a cross-country hike to reach it. Instead, *retrace your steps to the road junction at the start of this diversion, signed to Mount Wellington Mine, Fernysplat, Hicks Mill and Bissoe. Turn right there, and continue with the directions that follow.*

To omit the diversion, take the first left turning. Look left at the first gateway to see the outlines of a large mine pond on high ground quite close to the engine houses and the clock tower. Its prime function was to supply cooling water to the condensers of the United Mines' engines. It was kept full by Eldon's or "Little" engine [see footnote (13)], whose truncated engine house and stack can be seen 300 yd south of the road junction. On the opposite side of the road, where the buildings of Tregarlands Farm now stand, was a public house, the Miners' Arms. A right turn a short way past that leads to the conserved stamps-engine house **(14)** of Gwennap United, a short-lived operation around the year 1900. (See the note on the mines' history.) In front of the engine house - i.e. on the far side - is the massive concrete base of the stamps, and the gentle slope beyond that, now the site of a stock-car race track, was occupied by dressing floors. (See photograph 62 in J. Trounson's "Mining in Cornwall" Volume Two, which shows the interior of the vanner house.) Over to the right, near the entrance to a massive waste tip, is Eldon's engine house. Return to the road and continue as before. *Where the road curves left, at the point where the ruins of Garland's pumping-engine house* **(15)** *stand a little way back on the right, continue straight ahead on a track.*

10 *After about a quarter of a mile, turn left at the cross-tracks* - but first look over the gap in the hedge on the right at the opposite corner to see one of the best-preserved little round gunpowder houses in Cornwall. *The downhill track soon brings you back to the road.* On the right as you

---

(14) As you approach the house from the rear note the square opening for the steam pipe low down, proving that the boiler house was at the rear, a fairly common practice with stamps engines. This engine had a 34-inch cylinder and was purchased secondhand, probably from Killifreth Mine, all the engines from the main working which ended in 1870 having been scrapped.

(15) Garland's engine house has been occupied by two different pumping engines. It was built for an 85-inch engine pumping from the shaft just east of the surviving bob wall. For the Gwennap United operation a copious supply of water was needed for ore-dressing, so in about 1900 a secondhand 80-inch engine was purchased and installed in the then empty house. It had been built by Harvey & Co. in 1869 for Batters' Shaft at West Chiverton lead mine, near Zelah, where the engine house still stands. (A walk including West Chiverton is detailed in "Around St Agnes and Perranporth".) After a short period of work for Gwennap United the engine was sold to Condurrow United, south of Camborne, where, again, its house still stands. The rear of Garland's house and part of the stack were blasted down a few years ago because they were considered to be unsafe.

There is a ghost story associated with Garland's engine. It is said that one sunny evening, the engineman and his mate looked out of a window and noticed one of the shaftmen walking home across the burrows, with his underground clothes folded under his arm. Nothing strange about this, you may say - but the poor man had been killed in an accident in the shaft earlier in the day.

descend, some large dumps of mine waste are relics of Wheal Clifford.

11 *Turn right at the road.* (Another short diversion is suggested when you reach the side-road cutting back sharply on the left signed "Cusvey". After about 60 yards there is a low wire fence on the right, and if you step over that you will have a good view of Wheal Clifford whim shaft, used in recent years for ventilation by Mount Wellington Mine. Return to the road and turn left.) Continue down the road. The next left turning, with a small sign, "Old Cusvey House", would be a convenient way back to Twelveheads and your parking place, but we suggest you take another path, a little lower down the road, which provides more points of interest. As you walk on down the road, please take care: traffic here is rarely heavy, but can be fast. *The road bends left, passes the entrance to Mount Wellington Mine, then curves right.*

12 *At that point, take the path, signposted to Twelveheads, which is on the left and is partly blocked by several big granite blocks at the start.* Straight ahead now, on the far side of the valley, is part of the bob wall of the Nangiles Mine pumping-engine house, with massive burrows around it, containing much arseno-pyrite **(16)**. When the shaft was being inspected for possible re-use in the 1970s, safety considerations dictated demolition of the rest of the engine house and the stack which, up to that time, remained complete. *After about 50 yards, where the main track starts curving left, take the narrow path down on the right.* The first few yards tend to be rather overgrown, but after that it's clear, and as you approach the valley road you have a good view of the course of the Redruth and Chasewater Railway as it runs along a low embankment and crosses a stone bridge.

13 *At the road, turn left to return to the suggested parking place.* Soon you will pass a small layby on the right; opposite that is the unusual engine house of Wheal Andrew **(17)**, now converted to a dwelling. The house

---

(16) The pumping engine here was an 80-inch erected in 1862 and moved to Wheal Rose United, near Scorrier, in 1872. The presence of arsenic in this mine caused the water to be so acid that it was said that it would rot a man's boots off his feet. Following the closure of the modern Wheal Jane early in 1991, it was heavily polluted water from this section of the mine that gushed untreated into the Carnon River a year later when a concrete plug in the Nangiles adit gave way. Contact with salt water when it reached Restronguet Creek precipitated the ferric oxide in it, turning the Creek and parts of Carrick Roads into something resembling tomato soup; less dramatic but more damaging in the long term was the sudden increase in the levels of cadmium, zinc and other heavy metals. Most of the water from Nangiles is now (1994) heavily treated with lime - 20 tons every day - until the so-called "long-term solution" comes into operation, probably involving reed-beds and a sequence of deep and shallow ponds, rock filters, alkaline beds and a "polishing cell" in the Carnon valley below Bissoe.

(17) It contained a pumping engine of unusual form, probably with the beam underneath the cylinder, which drew from a shaft just in front of the end of the building which faces the road. Remains of the stack are at the rear. The house was inspected by one of the authors prior to conversion but tangible evidence such as engine mountings had been cleared out many years earlier to enable use as a barn. A few engines in Cornwall were inverted, i.e. the beam was arranged low down beneath the cylinder, because it saved on the height and cost of the engine house, but there were also drawbacks. In Scottish collieries, however, the arrangement was more frequently used.

called Wheal Andrew that comes next was the mine's count house. Just beyond that is a pair of parallel walls on the left, marking the point where the mineral line crossed the road. (From here to point 2 on the walk route the line runs through fields on the hill slope and is not available to walkers.) Another 50-or-so yards brings you back to the main layby.

The base of the Consols clock tower, January 1989

2
WHEAL KITTY, PENHALLS MINE
& BLUE HILLS MINE

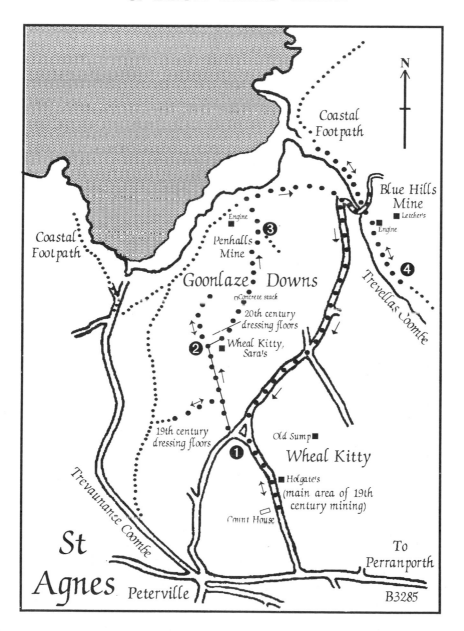

WHEAL KITTY, PENHALLS MINE & BLUE HILLS MINE

Only about a mile-and-a-half of walking is involved on this route, but there is quite a stiff climb near the end. Some of the tracks are distinctly puddly in typical Cornish weather, and one or two of the paths were partially overgrown with brambles when we walked them in September, so bring a stout stick and don't wear your best clothes.

This walk, amid dramatic clifftop and valley scenery, is full of interest for the mining history enthusiast. Goonlaze Downs and the deep valleys flanking them have yielded tin in plenty over a very long period, ranging from the streaming and shallow workings of the "old men" to deep mining that continued till 1930; even today, tin-bearing stone from mine dumps and the beach is still sometimes gathered, milled and smelted in Trevellas Coombe. In addition to two fairly complete engine houses there are very extensive dressing floors illustrating vividly many of the developments in the techniques for preparing ore for smelting that took place over the period from about 1850 to 1930. Evidence of streaming is particularly clear in Trevellas Coombe, where six heads of water-powered Cornish stamps are still in place and are readily visible from the footpath.

LOCATION (Wheal Kitty): Half a mile north east of St Agnes village. Grid reference: SW 726 510. OS maps: Pathfinder (1:25,000): No. 1352. Landranger (1:50,000): No. 204.

HOW TO GET THERE By car: Take the Perranporth road (B3285) from St Agnes. As you reach the edge of St Agnes, take the left turning signposted to Wheal Kitty. The easiest place to park is on the grassy triangle at the road junction you reach after about a quarter of a mile.

By public transport: There are infrequent bus services to St Agnes from Truro, St Ives, Camborne, Redruth, Perranporth and Newquay; see current timetables. Alight at Peterville and walk a short way along the Perranporth road. A few yards beyond the turning down to the beach (Trevaunance), turn sharp left on to Wheal Kitty Lane. After about a quarter of a mile this brings you to the parking place suggested above.

WALK DIRECTIONS AND DESCRIPTION OF MINING FEATURES

1 *Before starting the walk proper, it might be worth going a few yards along the road to the south (that is, back along the road by which we directed car drivers to come)* to look at the Wheal Kitty count house (now called the Old Count House), set back a little on the right. This was at the centre of the original site of the mine, as the area of disturbed ground on the opposite side of the road bears witness. The shaft north east of the count house is Holgate's, 110 fm deep, and Old Sump Shaft, on which a Sandys Vivian 50-inch pumping engine was installed in 1852, stood further north east. The engine worked until about 1910 when this part of the mine was abandoned, and was sold in 1912 to   *(Continuation is on page 39.)*

The 50-inch pumping engine at Old Sump Shaft, Wheal Kitty. The engine survives at Parkandillick clayworks where it was re-erected in 1912.

The view across Trevaunance Coombe and St Agnes from the generator/ compressor foundation, part of Wheal Kitty's 19th-century dressing floors.

WHEAL KITTY AND PENHALLS MINE

Goonlaze Downs (Cornish, *goon glas,* green downland), the high ground separating Trevaunance and Trevellas Coombes, had already been the source of "vast quantities of tin" when Thomas Tonkin wrote his notes on the parishes of Cornwall (1736), and the name "Pennals" (Cornish, cliff headland) appears on a map of the main lodes drawn three years earlier than that. Barncoat's map of 1838 shows "Penals" on the cliff edge and foreshore half way between the two coves, with "Higher Penals" and "Great Penals" just inland. At least fifteen other tin bounds on Goonlaze Downs are named, among them Wheal Kitty. By that time, according to Collins, Wheal Kitty was more than 50 fathoms deep and employed 258 people. The mine appears to have taken over the workings of various smaller adjoining concerns such as Wheal Pink, Goonlaze and Wheal Bottle or Vottle, but Penhalls, as it came to be called, continued as a separate and very successful unit until 1884. In its last 25 years it is said to have netted £100,000 in profits. A photograph dated c.1895, published in the Journal No.5 of the St Agnes Museum Trust (1989), shows the three empty Penhalls engine houses close to the cliffs overlooking Trevaunance Cove. Wheal Kitty worked continuously through to 1919, producing some copper and pyrite (iron) but mainly tin; Collins estimates that by 1910 the total output was worth at least £1m. - but he refers to periods of "adversity" as well as of "brilliant prosperity". In 1852 Copperhouse Foundry built a 50-inch pumping engine for Wheal Kitty, which was installed at Old Sump Shaft. Collins' own company bought the mine and also Penhalls in or soon after 1904, and in 1907 they launched Wheal Kitty and Penhalls United Ltd. In 1910 a new shaft, known as Sara's, was sunk at a central position and equipped with a 65-inch engine: see footnote 5 for details. Two years later the engine at Old Sump Shaft was sold to Parkandillick china clay works, near St Austell, where she still is and can be seen working, though not now under steam. The new enterprise met with only mixed fortunes, and closed in 1919. Seven years later a further attempt was made, this time with the intention of linking the workings with those on the other side of Trevaunance Coombe, such as West Kitty, Polberro and Wheal Friendly. The connection was achieved in 1929 at a depth of 842 ft below surface. By this time the old Wheal Kitty, Penhalls and Wheal Friendly sections were considered to be exhausted. What Trounson calls "the great *shoot* of tin under the valley between Wheal and West Kitty" was now in reach, but the 1930 slump in tin prices put a stop to further progress. Later in the decade attention was focused on Polberro, and attempts to locate the West Kitty lode by deepening the Turnavore Shaft there met with failure. Trounson believed that in fact it was found but not recognised, and that if more capital had been available Polberro could have been one of the great 20th century tin mines.

the Parkandillick china clay pit near St Dennis where it is now preserved. Little if anything remains of any mine buildings in this area. *Return the same way and continue ahead along the road towards the cliffs and the nearby group of old mine buildings.*

About 100 yards beyond the crossroads take the path# on the left which leads into the older mill and dressing floors (1) of Wheal Kitty. Up on the left at the start of this path are the remains of an embankment that carried a mine tramway. If you scramble up on to that it will lead you almost straight to the massive concrete bases of the mill's Californian stamps and of the building which housed the engine that powered them. If you keep to the path, with the embankment up on your left at first, look out for these things on your left: the rusty remains of what looks like part of a dome-ended boiler, but cannot be that because it is lined inside with bricks (a bit of a mystery here); nearby, a convex buddle in which, unusually, a fragment of the metal superstructure remains; next, the low ruins of a calciner, close to the path; and above that, the base of the Californian stamps; further away, protruding from a slope overgrown with gorse and bracken, the foundations of the older battery of Cornish stamps driven by the engine in the building which was destroyed by fire in 1905 (see accompanying photograph). The path continues downhill among more fragmentary and unidentifiable ruins of the dressing floors and brings you to old waste heaps of fine material from the floors, from which you have an excellent view of the Trevaunance valley, overlooked by the ruins of the Wheal Friendly engine house on the far side, with pillars that probably supported a stone crusher, and further away to the right the asbestos-roofed engine house of Turnavore Shaft, Polberro Mine.

Return the same way and turn left at the road. Soon after you have passed what looks like an outsize Nissen hut, currently in use for motor repairs, you reach the point where, on the left side of the road, until recently stood the transformer house used during the mine's last active period; that has now been demolished. Also gone is the boiler house for the horizontal winding engine, which stood on the right, near the stack which

---

(1) Owing to the level nature of the ground at Wheal Kitty, ore treatment was carried out on the edge of the Trevaunance valley. The concrete foundations visible here date from the turn of the century and belong to a set of Californian stamps which formed the basis of a tin mill which mainly employed buddles for ore concentration. The equipment was driven by a large 2-cylinder horizontal steam engine whose badly decayed engine beds, of concrete and masonry, stand just south of the stamps foundations. A slot in the concrete wall in front of the engine shows where the belt drive to the stamps ran through.

Of the earlier beam engine which drove Cornish stamps (on roughly the same site as the later Californians), all that can be seen is part of the masonry and concrete crankshaft foundation, including one flywheel slot. This stands a short distance south west of the mill engine foundation, surrounded by an impenetrable jungle of gorse. This engine suffered a serious fire in 1905 but was put back to work again for a few years before the Cornish stamp battery was replaced by the Californians about 1910.

Just north of the stamps, reduced masonry walls mark the site of a calciner battery dating from the 1870s, where the ore was roasted to recover the arsenic by-product. According to the 1878 edition of the OS map the flue from these ran south-eastwards to a stack of which all trace has vanished. The rusty cylinder referred to in the text may have been part of an Oxland & Hocking rotary calciner.

Wheal Kitty stamps engine rebuilt after the fire. Note the patch on the bob.

Wheal Kitty, 20th-century dressing floors, September 1993.
Sara's Shaft behind.

has survived. However, the building, with a black pitched roof, which housed the horizontal engine itself was still more-or-less intact in September 1993, but for how much longer? The same building also contained an air compressor for supplying underground rock drills.

2 *Where the road curves right towards the pumping engine house on Sara's Shaft, a brief diversion is recommended by continuing ahead towards the sea on a narrow path#,* which very soon brings you to the later mill and dressing floors **(2)** of Wheal Kitty. This installation dates from 1926 when the mine was reopened under new management and incorporated the then latest in dressing machinery. Photographs show the building to have been of impressive size. It was composed of corrugated sheets on a timber frame, typical of the period. Two masonry buildings on the north side of the mill housed Brunton calciners linked by a concrete flue to the square stack further north, visited later on the walk. *You might care to follow for a short distance the downhill track which heads roughly towards the distant bungalow up on the headland.* This brings you to the fines waste tip and West Pink Old Shaft, with a Clwyd cap. The bungalow (Blue Hills Cottage) is the rebuilt count house of Penhalls Mine when worked as an independent concern from the 1860s to 1884. In front of it, about 80 yards to the west, was the mine's Engine Shaft **(3)**, not easily visible, while to the right, further down the slope towards us, a few pieces of masonry are the sole remnants of Penhalls dressing floors. The stamps engine house stood on a mound some 60 yards south of the count house. In 1874 it suffered a serious fire, anticipating what was to happen at Wheal Kitty thirty years later. As a matter of interest, the Penhalls adit discharged at the east end of the beach at Trevaunance Cove. Though the entrance has fallen in, ochreous water may still be seen oozing from the cliff. Down in the dip between Penhalls and where we are standing a small isolated group of concrete ruins, including a large buddle, denotes the site of a tailings or slimes plant **(4)** associated with the Wheal Kitty mill.

Return the same way to the road and turn left past the horizontal winding

---

(2) The 1926 mill seems from the appearance of the concrete to have been constructed in two stages. The battery of Californian stamps stood on the row of deep slotted concrete plinths at the south end of the site and was driven electrically. The rest of the equipment consisted principally of shaking tables, a new development at the time, whose positions are marked by a series of small plinths.
After closure of the mine in 1930, the mill equipment was re-sited at Turnavore Shaft, Polberro Mine, across the valley to the west, where a similar set of foundations survives.
(3) The pumping engine on this shaft (80 fm deep) had a 50-inch cylinder and was built by Harvey & Co. of Hayle for the mine in 1863. After Penhalls' closure in 1884 the engine was moved to Trevaunance Mine, marked by a lone stack beside Beacon Drive nearly a mile west-south-west, and later to Gooninnis whose empty house with its stack truncated by a recent lightning strike can be seen on a hilltop south of St Agnes village. The engine's final move was to Goonvean China Clay pit where it still stands as a preserved but inaccessible industrial monument.
(4) Its purpose would have been to extract a further small quantity of tin oxide from the washwater leaving the mill proper. With the low tin prices prevailing in the 1920s, extracting the maximum would have been important. Recovery in such a mill would probably have been around 60-70%, the rest going to waste in the sea.

and compressor house and other mine buildings including a boiler house beside the Sara's (earlier known as West Pink) Shaft pumping engine house **(5)**. The shaft, 160 fm deep from surface and the mine's principal working shaft from 1910 onwards, lies just in front of the pumphouse but is now obscured. The burrow on the left, though still pretty impressive, has obviously been quarried, probably as a source of hardcore, perhaps for the construction of the road you are walking on, which was built quite recently to serve small industrial units around Sara's Shaft. This scheme aroused a good deal of local opposition, and seems to have been at least temporarily shelved; how much more demolition or mutilation of historic mine buildings it will involve if it does come about remains to be seen. *At the end of the road, continue ahead along a narrow and, when we explored it, rather overgrown path# which leads north-eastwards to Penhalls.* Shortly before joining a wider track leading to the garden gate of Blue Hills Cottage it passes close to the square, tapered arsenic stack previously referred to. Adjacent to the stack is the ruin of one of the access chambers, composed partly of masonry, giving rise to the supposition that it may have originated with Penhalls' own arsenic plant in the 1870s. Between the stack and the gate to the cottage on the left two mounds with a recess between mark the site of the Penhalls stamps engine mentioned earlier. *Once on the broad track turn right, away from the cottage.*

3 *Where the track reaches a T-junction, turn left, towards the sea.* In the fork are traces of one of the mine ponds, and somewhere hereabouts stood Penhalls' beam whim, which probably drew from several shafts. About 130 yards beyond the junction the ruined walls of a small square building on the right are remains of the mine's powder house. At this point you have a fine St Agnes mining panorama to your left, with St Agnes Beacon as the backdrop. On the left are the Sara's Shaft engine house and, much further away, the buildings of Gooninnis Mine, including an engine house with stack and another stack; further right, overlooking the valley, the

---

(5) The pumping engine here was installed in 1910 when the shaft was being deepened to serve the Wheal Kitty and Penhalls joint operation. It had a 65-inch cylinder and strokes of 10 ft in the cylinder and 9 ft in the shaft. It was built by the Perran Foundry in 1852 with a 60-inch cylinder and was purchased for Wheal Kitty after a spell standing derelict at Tindene Mine, near St Hilary. On being re-erected the steam jacket was dispensed with and the outer cylinder casting bored to the larger size. While increasing the engine's power, this move reduced its efficiency, leading to three boilers being required to supply steam.

The arrangement of valve gear and valve chests was untypical of a Cornish engine, being similar in these respects to the 70-inch engine designed by Hocking & Loam and preserved at the Prestongrange Mining Museum, near Edinburgh. Sara's engine stopped work in 1919 when the mine closed, but was restarted in 1926 and finally finished in 1930, by which time it was pumping from a depth of 950 ft below surface. Scrapping took place in 1938 but a fragment of the cast iron beam is preserved by the National Trust at East Pool. It was the last beam engine to work in the St Agnes district.

The boiler house bears evidence of having been extended as the shaft deepened and the load on the engine increased. It is unusual in that the boilers stood only slightly below the level of the engine cylinder. Normally the boilers stood sufficiently low for the condensate forming in the steam jacket to return to them by gravity, an arrangement not necessary when the engine cylinder was unjacketed.

Wheal Kitty: the 65-inch engine at Sara's Shaft just before the last working. On the left is the house for the Holman geared whim engine, and behind the headframe are the boiler houses.

The same buildings in September 1993

Wheal Friendly engine house; further away, on the northern slope of the Beacon, the lone stack of Trevaunance Mine; then the roofed engine house at the Turnavore Shaft of Polberro Mine, and further right again the stack of an arsenic burning house, also part of Polberro. *The track traverses the waste tip of Flat-rod Shaft* (6) *before dropping down to join the coastal footpath, where turn right.* If you look left before doing so, you can glimpse the headland on the west side of Trevaunance Cove, close to where St Agnes harbour once was; the cavernous opening in the cliff just above the two buildings is an ancient openwork mine known as Wheal Luna. On your right is a dramatic view of Trevellas Cove. *Follow the rough track down to Trevellas Coombe; the track is now used for motorcycle scrambling.*

After a few yards there is a small footpath at a slightly higher level on the left, and it is worth using that for the better view you get of Trevellas Coombe, where the valley floor is shaped by many centuries of tin-streaming. Today it is impossible to say whether the ruins visible at the seaward end of the valley belonged to Blue Hills Mine or local tin streamers. What is certain is that the equipment has seen many changes and Cornwall Archaeological Unit (Trevellas report dated 1986) noted the existence of an early tin smelter near the mouth of the coombe though its exact site is not known. The steep hillside opposite, known in the 18th century as Blowing House Hill, is criss-crossed by paths, many if not all of which were probably created by miners seeking tin: here and there you may be able to make out small exploratory shafts or adits. What looks like a length of rail from a mine tramway has been used for fencing between path and track shortly before you reach a wooden stile beside the ornate wrought-iron gate recently erected by the Motor Cycling Club.

Continue down and across the bridge to inspect the surface remains of Blue Hills Mine. Three obvious mining features may be seen downstream of the bridge. Nearest the sea is a masonry waterwheel pit which doubtless worked a few heads of tin stamps. Next comes an interesting mine stack of the old "telescope" pattern (7). The stack has obviously been altered during its life and could have been associated with a burning house, calciner or even a small steam engine. Close to the road are two partly overgrown settling ponds. The substantial masonry ruin on the east side of the road is the crankshaft loading of a horizontal steam engine of Blue Hills Mine which drove tin stamps at night and hauled ore from various shafts during the day (8).

---

(6) Flat-rod Shaft is so named because pumps in it were worked by flat-rods running across the ground from the pumping engine. It is 40 fm deep.

(7) So-called telescope stacks were common in Cornwall in the late 18th/early 19th centuries and appear on many of the Abandoned Mine Plans. The name derives from the steps or sudden reductions in diameter which occur as the height increases. This one has only one step but the best-known surviving example, at the old Pednandrea mine in Redruth, has seven - as originally built it had twelve! The design reflects the Cornish practice of reducing the thickness of the stack towards the top, for economy. A smooth exterior as normally used later makes the structure less vulnerable to damage by strong winds, ivy growth etc.

(8) The use of a beam or a horizontal engine for more than one function was once common

A few yards to the right of the engine foundation, a gate leads to a broad track running up the valley. On the right of this track a tall burrow is the waste tip from Blue Hills Engine Shaft, while the house of the 70-inch beam engine which pumped from it is on the left **(9)**. The shaft itself has been filled and shows as a shallow depression among the bushes in front of the engine house. Just north of the shaft twin blocks of masonry with a slot between carried the engine's balance bob, and it is probable that flat-rods were carried from it to Letcher's Shaft, 47 yards away up the hill. The chimney stack on the hill slope was linked to the engine's boiler house by a flue, and served both the pumping engine and the whim; the boiler house itself, with two Cornish boilers set low down, was on the far side of the house.

BLUE HILLS MINE

Several old tin mines including Wheal Glynn, Wheal Joy, Nanpatha, Wheal Pink, Goonlaze and Wheal Dellick, which were all linked underground and together are reported to have made profits of over £100,000, amalgamated under the name of Blue Hills in 1810. Before that they had been drained by means of waterwheels, but in 1810 a 57-inch steam engine previously used in Gwinear parish was installed to pump at Blue Hills, and Richard Trevithick was employed as engineer until 1814. The tin was dressed by no fewer than nine sets of water-powered stamping mills. By 1819, when the mine seems to have closed, it had reached a depth of 40 fathoms. It was reopened about 1858. In the next forty years the mine sold 2,117 tons of black tin for £116,746. There is evidence of a restart in 1869 with 5,000 shares, the cost book indicating the purchase of a 60-inch engine at that time. This must later have been enlarged or replaced. Following financial difficulties caused by the slump in tin prices early in the 1870s, in 1879 Blue Hills came under the same management as Penhalls Mine, with which it had become interconnected underground in 1876. During the following decade, Blue Hills was at its most prosperous but Penhalls declined, and in 1893 its sett was divided between Blue Hills and Wheal Kitty. When Blue Hills finally closed as a separate entity, in 1897, it was 100 fathoms deep and employed 100 people. It was reworked along with Penhalls and Wheal Kitty early this century, but is said not to have yielded any significant amount of tin then.

---

in mining but the precise mechanics of how it was done are often unclear. The Blue Hills whim/stamps engine had the cylinder and the driver enclosed in the house but the connecting rod passed through an opening in the front wall and the crank and flywheel were in the open. The boiler house was on the right (east) side and the flue led to the stack part-way up the hillside.

(9) There is not much on record about this engine but measurements of the house confirm that its cylinder diameter was 70 inches and its strokes quite long, 11 ft in the cylinder and 10 ft in the shaft. It was probably installed in the 1860s when the mine was being re-invigorated, and worked until closure in 1898. The lack of any dressed granite blocks or tie-rods to strengthen the bob wall is surprising in so large an engine. This and the lack of windows probably indicate a cash shortage on the part of the adventurers. The shaft is vertical for a depth of 66 fm below adit and on the underlie to 96 fm.

Blue Hills Mine, September 1993: the 70-inch pumping-engine house

Remains possibly of a burning house by the telescope stack in Trevellas Coombe; Blue Hills Mine in background. (August 1989)

Continuing along the track for a few yards beyond the engine house, the site of buddles and other equipment for dressing beach tin is passed on the right. The streamworks continued long after the mine itself closed and probably used the mine's old equipment. On the hillside to the left large undisturbed waste tips are a good indication of the amount of mining carried on here.

Keeping to the path or track, walk a short way up the valley, past a bungalow and fish tanks, to see one of the very few sets of Cornish stamps still in situ. Just before you reach them you will see, propped against the wall beneath the track, a dismantled waterwheel brought from Penzance about 1984 or 1985. Six heads of stamps remain in place; it appears that the machine originally had twelve in two groups of six rather than the normal arrangement of three groups of four. Tin streaming and smelting are still carried out by members of the Wills family in this part of Trevellas Coombe, although while tin prices remain low other sources of income like fish farming are needed. A visit by members of the Trevithick Society in 1987 was reported by Kenneth in the Society's Newsletter No. 59 as follows: "He (Mr Colin Wills) enthralled the party by describing how he and his son derive a living from holding the beach rights and extracting tin from stones found on the beach or fallen from the cliffs. His deft demonstration of *vanning,* using an ordinary shovel, and description of his home-made smelter from which he produces small ingots for sale were an eye-opener for most of the party! He also showed us an early calciner now used as a store, and we came away feeling that arts associated with tin that we had considered lost are not only being revived, but are in very capable hands."(10)

(The walk further up the valley, by the way, is a beautiful one and full of mining interest: at "Jericho", for instance, close to where the B3285 crosses it, was a large tin-mill belonging to West Kitty Mine. Very little of Jericho Stamps, as it was called, is visible now even though it was in use until well into this century. See *Around St Agnes & Perranporth,* Walk 7.)

4 *Return the same way, back across the stream, and take the steep road,* which gives you another fine view of the valley, with its various mine buildings, dumps and old shafts. When the road eventually levels off you will see the Sara's Shaft buildings to your right, and the rough ground on your left, now colonised by gorse and heather, is the site of the earliest workings of Wheal Kitty. *The road soon returns you to the suggested parking place.*

---

(10) In a discussion with Ted Gundry and Bob on Radio Cornwall in May 1994, Mr Wills estimated that over some 16 years his family produced 80-100 tons of tin concentrate in the valley. Their experiments with smelting involved using bits of a bicycle, a sheet of galvanised iron for a chimney, and the inner tube of a tractor for bellows! "Each time the bellows puffed the air into the fire the chimney used to belch flames and smoke like a dragon," he remembered. He and his son Mark have plans to restore the wheel and stamps, and he looks forward to the day when he will at last "hear the sound of the old stamp-heads thumping down." They hope before long to open their premises to the public - preferably walkers, as access to the valley for cars is poor - to see tin streaming in progress. When this will be is uncertain as we go to press, but the telephone number for enquiries is 0872-553341.

3
TYWARNHAYLE MINE
& WHEAL ELLEN

It is not possible to include all the surface remains of these mines on one round walk. Instead we suggest a short circular tour of the sites on high ground, together with separate visits to places of interest on the lower slopes and in the valley. Little more than a mile of walking is involved unless you choose to extend the circular tour to include a section of the coast road north-east of Porthtowan: see section 5 in the directions for details. Both Tywarnhayle Mine and Wheal Ellen have a great deal to offer to those interested in Cornish mining history, and their setting is very splendid: from the vantage point of John's Shaft you have fine views, both coastal and inland; the gorse and heather on the hill slopes are breathtaking, especially in the autumn; and the valley running south east from Porthtowan has a stark beauty of its own. The paths and tracks are mostly in good condition, but the one up to Taylor's Shaft is little-used and tends to be rather overgrown. Refreshments are available from shops, pubs and seasonal cafés in nearby Porthtowan, and another pub, the Victory Inn, is a short way north-east on the coast road.

LOCATION About half a mile south east of Porthtowan. Grid reference for first parking place: SW 696 474. OS maps: Pathfinder (1:25,000) Nos. 1359 & 1360; Landranger (1:50,000) No. 203.

HOW TO GET THERE By car: If approaching Porthtowan by the coast road, turn inland just east of the road which leads down to the village and beach. The road you want runs in a deep valley and heads south east. After about 100 yards, park in the layby on the left. If you are arriving via the exit from the A30 at Scorrier and Wheal Rose, you will find this parking place on your right as you approach the coast road. **By public transport:** There are occasional buses to Porthtowan from Camborne, Portreath, Redruth and Truro. See current timetables. Alight near the Porthtowan Garage on the coast road rather than down at the beach, and walk up the valley road just mentioned.

WALK DIRECTIONS AND DESCRIPTION OF MINING FEATURES

1 Before you leave the suggested parking place, look up the canyon-like valley with its rushing stream and you will see evidence of mining on both sides. On the left is Tywarnhayle Mine, an extensive sett of which the part we can see was originally known as Wheal Rock. On the right, a few shafts further up the valley belong to Wheal Music, a copper producer of 1815-25. The lodes of the mines in this area cross the valley diagonally, approximately east-west, rendering precise delineation of the sett boundaries difficult. Also on the right of the valley you will notice the embankment of a leat which took water from the stream further up and delivered it into a headpond, the site of which is now concealed in the bushes behind the small modern pumping station building. The leat

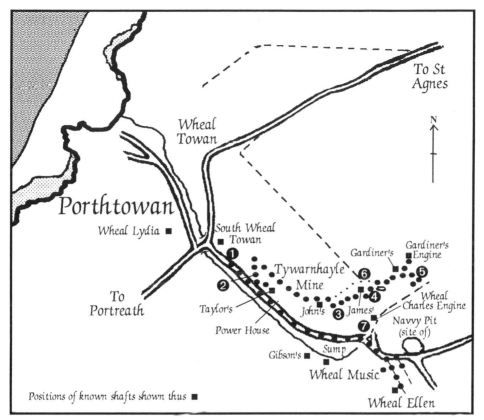

supplied a grist mill in the 18th century and the headpond was utilised later to power waterwheels downstream of the present bridge carrying the coast road, where the old maps show an iron smelter and a later grist mill. On the left side of the valley another, less distinct, leat can be seen leading towards Wheal Towan, one of the major copper producers of this area, which is closer to the beach. This probably served waterwheels on South Wheal Towan after Wheal Towan's closure in 1835. Notice the mine's chimney perched on the slope near the corner (known locally as Echo Corner). South Wheal Towan produced 24,161 tons of copper ore in the period 1817-74. Old photographs show two stacks close together here. There was a 70-inch pumping engine beside a shaft a few yards north of the stack, but only the shaft is left, on private land and not visible from the road (1).

(1) The massive granite bedstones on which the cylinder of an earlier 40-inch engine at Echo Corner stood are now on display at the entrance to the St Agnes Museum. Most unusually, they reveal two sets of bolt holes, one for about a 60-inch cylinder and one for the 40-inch, as if the engineers who installed the engine used bedstones secondhand from a bigger engine. The square, rusty outline of the cylinder bottom of the 40-inch engine is also discernible. (The museum is at the south end of the village.) The 70-inch engine at

Start the visit to Tywarnhayle Mine by walking up the valley road till you reach the narrow path# ahead on the left which leads up to the ruinous pumping engine house at Taylor's Shaft. This path was rather overgrown when we used it, but it's worth risking a few scratches in order to take a close look at this building and the other mining features near it **(2)**. WARNING: the engine house is in an advanced state of decay, and the bob wall in particular looks like collapsing quite soon unless stabilising work is carried out. Please heed the "Danger" sign and do not attempt to enter the building.

Echo Corner worked until 1847 when it was advertised for sale along with an 18-inch winding engine (which probably accounts for the second chimney stack) and three waterwheels driving tin stamps and copper crushers. At that time South Wheal Towan had been working in conjunction with Wheal Lydia, a little-known, shallow copper mine. Its run of shafts extends in a north-easterly direction from Lydia Shaft, the main one, which may be seen a little way up the north-facing hill slope on the far side of the crossroads. Close to it a chimney stack once stood, serving an iron smelter in the valley below, where the new housing stands. From 1849 South Wheal Towan was incorporated in the Tywarnhayle sett.

(2) The house is of exceptional interest in that the 58-inch pumping engine which occupied it had a wooden beam. It stood many years derelict after stopping in about 1852 and is said to have been the last survivor with a wooden beam in Cornwall. The shaft in front from which it pumped is 80 fathoms deep below adit and should be approached with care, if at all. The stack is separate, to the west of the house which, unusually, is set back into the steep hillside and so lacks the usual large doorway at driver's floor level by which the main parts were normally taken into the house. Here the cylinder would have been taken over the shaft and in through the oversize "plug doorway" in the bob wall, whose wooden lintel is now showing its age. Further, the beam opening above does not extend the full width of the house but is merely a wide slot in the bob wall, reflecting the narrowness of the wooden beam which would have had a kingpost and bridle rod strengthening.

The Abandoned Mine Plans (preserved at the Cornwall Record Office) show a most unusual arrangement of flat-rods by which the engine was also able to pump from James' Shaft, some 380 yards to the north-east. These rods were attached to the main beam and ran through the window-like opening high up in the rear wall. From there they passed along a trench which may be seen later running up the hillside before taking a 45° right turn turn towards James' Shaft.

The engine itself is said to have come from Lambo Mine in Gwinear parish in 1826 and to have worked on two different sites at Tywarnhayle.

Taylor's Shaft is also famous in the annals of Cornish mining as having been the site of the first submersible electric pump in Cornwall. This was a cumbersome machine, as shown by a well-known published photograph of its being lowered down the shaft in 1906. Current to it was supplied by gas-engine generators based in the red-roofed building beside the road below the shaft. It was used in a short-lived reworking for low-grade copper ore in the shallow levels and succeeded in lowering the water to the 40-fathom level below adit. However it suffered from impeller corrosion due to the acid water it was handling, a problem shared with other electric pumps in Cornwall until better materials became available.

The concrete foundations close to the stack are of an electric hoist used in the 1906 reworking.

It is just possible that a Richard Trevithick 12-inch cylinder "puffing" (i.e. non-condensing) pumping engine supplied to the mine in 1809 was also erected on Taylor's Shaft, but it is more likely to have stood on Old Engine Shaft which Dines says is sited 70 yards SSE of Taylor's. As so often happens in Cornwall, all evidence of it has been obscured by later mining operations.

Tywarnhayle Mine, September 1993: Taylor's 58-inch pumping-engine house

TYWARNHAYLE MINE

Tywarnhale, Tywarnhaile or Tywarnhayle (Cornish, *ti war an hayle,* house on the estuary) is really the name of an ancient manor, but is used to refer to a group of copper mines whose workings were combined. Wheal Rock was working at least as far back as 1750. In 1809 it was bought by Andrew Vivian, who renamed it United Hills. He installed a "little puffing engine" with a 12-inch cylinder, made by his partner, Richard Trevithick. After heavy losses, the mine was closed in 1815. A new company reopened it in 1826, installing a 58-inch engine (exactly where is uncertain), and later an 80-inch one at Gardiner's. This period witnessed two serious accidents, both caused by bursting boilers. The first, in 1827, caused no deaths but showered bricks and other debris into the valley. On Wednesday 3rd February 1830, nine people were killed, including a boy and a girl, when a boiler which had only recently been repaired at Redruth Hammer Mill exploded, completely without warning. Seven of the victims had been warming themselves before starting work. A dramatic and detailed account of this accident is in Cyril Noall's book, *Cornish Mine Disasters.* The mine was at its most prosperous in the late 1830s; between 1836 and 1850, the depth of the workings increased from 36 to 100 fathoms below adit, and in the period 1826-52, 67,462 tons of copper ore were raised, according to the surviving records. Further losses led to closure in 1852. A new attempt was made in 1859, but despite the report in the *Western Daily Mercury* of 26 March 1864, claiming that "there is little doubt that Tywarnhaile Mine will be one of the best copper mines in the country", this venture closed down later that same year (1864). In 1906 yet another company began work here, concentrating on the low-grade copper still remaining in the surface dumps and the shallow levels. It erected the power house by the road, and used coal brought from Portreath to manufacture gas, which in turn powered generators to supply electricity to the new pump at Taylor's Shaft. This was the first electrically driven centrifugal pumping system used in Cornwall, and another novelty was an Elmore oil vacuum plant, installed at the same time. Mr J.Elmore, the inventor of this flotation process, was a director of the company. Hopes were high that it would enable economic recovery of the ore, but, despite alterations to the plant, it was a commercial failure, and the mine closed in 1907. Since 1908, apart from a period during World War 2, Tywarnhayle has been in use to train students from the Royal School of Mines, Imperial College, London. The School owns or leases all the workings of Tywarnhayle, and groups of students usually spend five weeks of their course here.

For further detail about the history of this mine, see the article by Dr Robin Smith, originally published in the Royal School of Mines Journal and reprinted in the Journal of the St Agnes Museum Trust, No. 4 (1988). Several of the above details are derived from it.

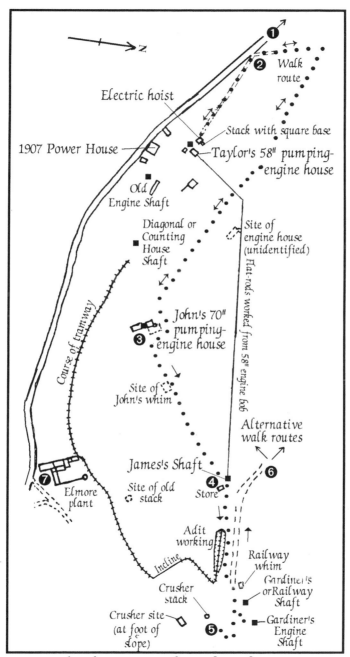

Tywarnhayle Mine - Plan of Surface Remains

2 *Now go back down the same path, but not right down to the road: take the path# almost straight ahead which climbs quite steeply.* After a sharp right turn you will pass a small quarry which is above the Taylor's Shaft engine house and was probably the source of much of the stone for that and other nearby mine structures. Try lining yourself up with the axis of Taylor's engine house and then look up the hillside left of the path. You should see part of the trench which carried the flat-rods to James' Shaft. Below the path a little further on are the low stone walls and foundations of quite a large rectangular building which is said to have been the mine's count house. A track to it running up the hillside from further up the valley can be seen from below. As you approach the magnificently-sited pumping engine house at John's Shaft (known also at different times as Turton's or Haynes'), notice the various traces of mining activity close to the path. On the right a short stone revetted embankment projects out above the steep slope down to the road. Its probable purpose was to dump copper ore down a chute into waiting carts on the count house access track below; traces of stone setts for cart wheels can be seen crossing the path here. The levelled areas on the left of the path are the sorting floors where stones of copper were hand picked from the rock being trammed from John's Shaft. The waste was simply dumped on the hillside. Traces of cobbled areas in the path are the spalling floors where large stones were broken down by "bal maidens" or other surface workers using heavy hammers. There are traces of leats nearby, and these are even more obvious at the higher level further left. Above that again is a rectangular hollow, now overgrown with gorse, which was a reservoir, a common cooling pond for John's engine and an engine to the west which was probably a copper crusher. John's engine would have had a "house lift" to keep the engine pond topped up.

3 *After inspecting the John's Shaft engine house* (3) *and the other*

---

(3) John's engine house was built in 1861 for a secondhand 70-inch pumping engine from Great Hewas tin mine, near St Austell. This engine had an exceptionally long piston stroke of 12 ft and a 10 ft 6 in stroke of the rods in the shaft. After finishing work at Tywarnhayle in 1864 the engine was purchased by the Wheal Uny (Redruth) adventurers and erected there in 1872. Its engine house there, too, may still be seen.

Interesting features at John's Shaft are the walled enclosure for the engine's balance bob, doubtless considered necessary because of the exposed site, and the depression north of the house marking the site of the boiler house with its three Cornish boilers. The flue entry in the base of the chimney stack was still visible when we visited the engine house, showing that the boilers were staked from the east end, nearest the shaft. This has been filled, but we don't know how securely. Its position in front of the engine house is marked by an upstanding masonry plinth on the south edge which supported one leg of the maintenance shear over the shaft. In line with the shear legs north of the shaft can be discerned the circular level area or plat where the manual capstan was sited, with a masonry-lined depression in the centre where the rope drum was. Part of the rope trench to the shears can also be seen. Evidence of maintenance equipment such as this is quite rare in Cornwall.

Down in the valley below, directly opposite John's engine and marked by two electricity pylons, is a large burrow surrounding Sump Shaft of Wheal Music. Active in the years 1815-1825, this shaft has clearly contained pumping equipment but whether water- or steam-driven cannot be confirmed. Probably a steam engine superseded a waterwheel within the life of the mine. *(Footnote continues on page 57.)*

Tywarnhayle Mine, September 1993: John's 70-inch pumping-engine house.
Note the boiler-house flue leading into the base of the stack.

Tywarnhayle Mine: looking across the shaft at the walled enclosure for the balance bob at John's 70-inch pumping-engine house

structures surrounding it, walk uphill, on a stony path# which passes among small waste heaps. Almost at the top of the slope you will come to a pit about ten feet deep - not evidence of an old shaft, but the site of the John's Whim engine house. When this was demolished, even the foundations were removed - hence the pit. *Continue in the same direction towards the small stone building,* now used as a "crib hut" (rest house and shelter for the mining students). Just to the left of that is James' Shaft, 80 fathoms deep and partly on an incline; it was used for pumps worked by flat-rods from Taylor's old engine in the 1850s. Also close to the crib hut is the displaced foundation of an electric hoist, probably dating from 1906-7, lying half on its side, and a white-painted survey datum point. The timber cover and metal framework at the mouth of James' Shaft reflect the fact that this is one of the access points to the mine used by the students, like the next two shafts we shall see.

4 *Continue on the path to the right of the hut* to the wooden fence above a small cutting leading to a mine portal. The gulley, along which once ran a tramway, is rather overgrown, but you may be able to push your way through to the timberwork across the portal which bars the way but allows you a glimpse of the underground workings. This portal was used in 1906-7 for tramming low-grade ore to the head of an incline down to the treatment plant. *Walk downhill on the curving track#.* Soon you will see, down to your right, the top of a truncated mine stack, and on the left at this point is the wooden entrance to Gardiner's or Railway Shaft. A steam whim used to stand beside the path just south of the shaft. A 50-yard detour along the small uphill path# which starts in front of the shaft leads to Gardiner's (or Williams') Engine Shaft **(4)**. This, too, has a wooden cover. It is the deepest shaft on the mine, extending to 100 fathoms below adit. *Finally continue down the main track* to the ore-storage area, from which presumably chutes were used to deliver the ore down the steep slope to the lane and copper-crushing plant below **(5)**.

Higher up the hillside and round the shoulder to the left can be seen the burrows of South Wheal Ellen, while in the bottom of the valley nearer at hand is the engine house with a castellated stack of Ellen United which we will explore later.

(4) Two large pumping engines have stood on the overgrown level area west of this shaft. The first was an 80-inch, one of the high-duty engines designed by Sam Grose, moved from Druce's Shaft on nearby Wheal Towan in about 1840. It was later removed, and for the 1860 reworking a 70-inch engine was erected on the same spot. A similar engine to John's, it, too, was a product of the St Austell Foundry, and had been new to Wheal Tristem (or Tristram) tin mine near St Austell in 1853. (The 1856 sale notices of Wheal Tristem, by the way, went into great detail and included a feather bed!) The 70-inch was known as "Louisa's Engine" following a naming ceremony in February 1860 in recognition of Lady Louisa Falconer's perseverance in opening the mine. The shaft is vertical only for the first ten fathoms; then it follows a westward underlie down to the 100-fathom level. Because the shaft is on high ground the adit is 33 fathoms below the surface at this point and so keeps a large part of the mine drained - one of the reasons why it is attractive for teaching underground surveying in the dry, cavernous old copper stopes.

(5) Evidence suggests that there were actually two crusher engines serving the mine. The 1st edition OS map shows an engine house yards to the north of John's, on the northern end of the rectangular pond, still visible, which probably provided cooling water for both

The stack already mentioned belonged to the beam crusher engine whose boiler house was connected to the stack by an inclined flue. This engine, with crusher house attached, of which no trace remains, stood to the left (east) of the nearer cottage. Unfortunately the stack was shorn of its top brickwork a few years ago for safety reasons and now gives a false impression of its original height. The cleverly-designed retaining walls to keep the mine waste from sliding down the hillside are a notable feature here. The main track ends suddenly at a large waste tip which has been partly dug away exposing a large bank of cinders near the top. Clearly this is where they were tipped from the boiler houses of the two pumping engines on Gardiner's Shaft. Across the valley from this area, looking east and just below the road to Mount Hawke, can be seen the recently filled in pit known as Navvy Pit **(6)**, worked early in the 19th century as part of Wheal Music. The faint course of a leat may be seen running from higher up the valley, past the pit and under the Mount Hawke road. Left of the sewage works are the old burrows of Wheal Fancy, one-time part of Tywarnhayle, while further up the valley are the more distant burrows of East Tywarnhayle mine.

5 *Return the same way at first, but this time keep to the main track until you have passed the hut on your left.*

6 Here you have two choices:

Either (a): Keep to this track, which continues for about half a mile and eventually meets the coast road above Porthtowan; turn left on that, and at the foot of the steep hill left again to return to the parking place. The drawbacks of this route are that it is rather longer; the half mile of track at the start is rather dull and featureless; and the main road can be uncomfortably busy in summer. On the other hand, if you walk on the right as you descend the hill you have a fine view, not only of the coast but, just below you, of the site of the crusher floors and the remains of the burrows of another rich mine, Wheal Towan **(7)**. You will also see a nicely-

---

engines. It appears likely that copper ore was sorted, spalled, crushed and despatched from both parts of the mine, in which case the unexplained engine near John's would have driven the other crusher.

(6) Navvy Pit, about an acre in area and 150 feet deep, was in its latter years used as a rubbish tip - a fate which currently threatens the last few remaining examples of openwork mining in Cornwall. The copper lodes at shallow levels here were "split up into minute strings and branches, none of which were singly worth pursuit. The whole rock was then removed and the copper ores extracted" (Henwood, 1857-9). All this openwork mining seems to have been done before 1833, and one early commentator stated that profits of £100,000 were made. In 1980 a company named Wheal Concord Ltd was formed to explore for tin on the site of an old mine of the same name near Blackwater; by 1982, 21,000 tonnes of ore had been raised by the workforce of forty, and the waste materials were dumped in Navvy Pit, thus partially hiding not only the rubbish but also the pit itself, one of the most impressive relics of mining in the area. Before the process was complete, Wheal Concord became a victim of the 1985 slump in tin prices, but during the past three or four years further infilling has been done and the surface landscaped.

(7) The shafts of Wheal Towan run parallel to, and on the seaward side of, the coast road towards St Agnes, but they and the once extensive burrows have been largely obliterated in recent years. The mine was a major copper producer in the years 1815-35 and became

Tywarnhayle Mine in the 1890s: Gardiner's 70-inch pumping (right) and whim engine houses on hilltop, with the copper crusher beside the cottages below. The man just visible in the foreground left of centre appears to be standing on the edge of Navvy Pit.

The copper-crusher stack as it is a century later.

restored engine house with its truncated chimney stack down amongst the seaside cottages on the far side of the valley **(8)**.

Or (b): Turn sharp left on a slightly narrower track or path heading back towards the John's Shaft engine house. For much of the way, this track runs quite close to a stone hedge on your right. At the point where the track curves a little to the left, the small pit on your right may mark the former position of one of the supports for the flat-rods running from Taylor's engine house to James' Shaft. *Keep to the track as it zigzags behind the engine house, and soon you are back on the path by which you came up earlier.*

Now to see the other surface remains of Tywarnhayle and Wheal Ellen, *when you get down to the valley road turn left.* (Alternatively, you could return to your car and drive up the road, thus saving yourself perhaps a little over half a mile on foot: there is room to park at point 7 on the sketch map: on the left just before the road curves right and left, close to the Wheal Ellen engine house with its castellated chimney. We recommend walking, however, despite the fact that this road can be quite busy: only that way can you fully appreciate the special beauty of this stark landscape and the impact on it of all the attempts that have been made to exploit the copper beneath it.)

The buildings you soon pass on the left of the road are used by the Royal School of Mines in London for students when on fieldwork. The largest building, with its red roof, is the powerhouse which contained three gas-engine generators supplying current to the submersible pump for the 1906-7 reworking. In the yard just to the east is another boarded-over shaft. This leads only down to the adit which discharges water into the stream and through which students have to wade to obtain underground access.

On the opposite side of the valley, close to the road, the large waste tip with a flat top betrays the site of Sump Shaft of Wheal Music, already referred to. It is not readily accessible.

7 About 300 yards past the powerhouse, a layby on the left with some masonry and concrete ruins on the hillside above marks the site of the Elmore oil vacuum plant for treating the low-grade copper ore, used in the 1906-7 working **(9)**. The concrete beds of a double cylinder mill engine which drove the plant can be seen by scrambling a short distance up the slope just to the right of the ruins. Higher up stand a concrete tank and

---

famous in 1827 for its two 80-inch pumping engines, Wilson's and Druce's, designed by Samuel Grose, which achieved record efficiency figures for the time.

(8) Built in 1872 for an ill-fated venture called New Wheal Towan to exploit the old workings of Wheal Lushington on the hill behind, the house was never occupied by an engine. The engine (secondhand from Ireland) was left to rust in the open when the cash ran out. In more recent years the building served as a café and is now a dwelling tastefully restored as far as possible to its original condition. The adit behind the house through which it was intended to run flat-rods to work pumps has been blocked off. Old plans show the adit to pass through the hill and emerge at the foot of the cliffs beyond.

(9) The process used is known as "flotation". The separation of ore from unwanted material is achieved by forming a froth to which the ore particles cling.

the stump of a stack marking the site of a single Lancashire boiler which supplied steam to the engine. One can only marvel at the ingenuity of engineers who perched heavy equipment on a steep slope like this.

A little above the plant, level tracks running around the hillside contour carried a narrow-gauge tramway. This enabled ore to be trammed to the plant from Taylor's Shaft in the west and the foot of the incline from the portal near James' Shaft in the other direction.

About 60 yards north east of the Elmore plant, at about the same contour as the tramway, is the engine shaft of Wheal Charles which at one time was a separate concern. Pumping was effected by a rotary engine driving flat-rods, later sold off. The area is now overgrown and inaccessible.

Continuing up the road as it curves to the right and then left, you soon find yourself approaching the fine engine house of Wheal Ellen with the peculiar castellated top to the chimney stack. There are three tracks leading off to the right as one ascends the hill - the middle one is the best for getting a closer view. The whole area around the engine house is reasonably accessible, with patches of small gorse and heather **(10)**. The waste tips here, once extensive, were removed during World War 2 to construct local airfield runways.

The ruins of the 1907 working lie some 50 yards east of the engine house and consist of a sadly-decayed concrete office building and the foundations of a producer gas plant and gas engine driving a small flotation plant. This was used in an abortive attempt to treat the complex copper/zinc ores believed to be lying on the dumps. Some of the small coal used to feed the plant may still be found in the vicinity.

There are also remains to be seen of earlier work at Wheal Ellen using water power, but it has not been possible to date these beyond saying that they appear on the 1st (1878) edition of the OS map. To explore these, start at the point where the uppermost of the three tracks mentioned earlier leaves the road by the sign "Wheal Basset Farm". The sign actually stands

---

(10) Like the house at New Wheal Towan (already referred to), this one also never had an engine inside. It was built by a Manchester-based company in 1866 for a long (12 ft) stroke 70-inch pumping engine then standing idle at Boscawen Mine (beside the main railway line near Blackwater). A ceremony to lay the foundation stone was held on 31st March in that year. In the following June more shares were advertised on the strength of an alleged discovery of a rich lode of copper (27.5%) in the new shaft. That is the last we hear of the concern which went under the grandiose title of Ellen United Copper and Zinc Mining Company. The Trevithick Society's founder, the late Mr W. Tregoning Hooper, used to say that the house was built by his uncle who received not a penny piece for his work! The unusual stack was said to be identical to the one at Wheal Golden, on the cliffs near Penhale Camp, Holywell, where it and the engine house were flattened during World War 2, as they were though to be a landmark which could help guide enemy aircraft. The Boscawen 70-inch engine, incidentally, remained boarded up and greased in its house for a few more years until it was sold to the Van Mine at Llanidloes in mid-Wales where it gave good service into the present century.

Prior to this short-lived attempt, Wheal Ellen had produced 24,000 tons of copper ore in the period 1826-62. The stated intention of the 1866 company was to work the mine in conjunction with Wheal Music and to explore the ground beneath Navvy Pit. This has never been done, but the year 1907 saw another brief attempt to open up the complex copper-zinc ores for which the mine was noted.

on an elevated section of a leat which conveyed water to waterwheels, such evidence being rare in Cornwall. On the opposite (north) side of the track are two headponds at slightly different elevations. Reference to the old maps indicates that the upper one was fed by the leat which skirted Navvy Pit. The lower one took water from a leat originating below the corn mill at Manor Parsley, about half a mile up the valley leading eastwards, whose course is still clearly visible. The upper pond seems to have been used to top up the lower one when required, while the lower one fed the wheels.

About 30 yards west of the "Wheal Basset Farm" sign, the sudden ending of the embankment and some stonework mark the site of the pit for an overshot waterwheel which was used to work a set of stamps. Close to the wheelpit on the south side, rusty iron fishplates projecting from the ground are the remains of the wooden framing, probably of steam stamps.

The tailrace from the wheel can be traced through the gorse and heather for some 70 yards to the remains of another wheelpit. The purpose of the wheel here is less certain, but it probably augmented the crushing or stamping capability of the upper one. Another 30 yards further on three sadly reduced stone structures appear to consist of two small ore roasters or calciners, possibly for the recovery of arsenic, with a chamber of indeterminate purpose between them. The easterly one shows traces of firebrick inside which a pivoted hearth rotated. The westerly one is better preserved and though the internals are obscured by fallen debris, on the outside can be seen rusty projecting bolts to which cast iron ties would have been fixed, to help the masonry resist the heat without cracking. A depression in the ground on the south side of these structures probably indicates the site of an undershot waterwheel to drive the calciners' revolving hearths. Between this wheelpit and the second waterwheel upstream the leat has been culverted for part of the distance. Close by a bank of slimes suggests that the ore was buddled after being stamped or crushed. The 2nd edition OS map (1906) shows what appear to be two ruined Brunton calciners about 40 yards SE of the present older ruins, and probably also waterwheel-driven. Paradoxically there is no sign of them today; possibly they were removed stone by stone for use elsewhere.

The leat serving Wheal Music Sump Shaft left the stream south of the present area of disturbed ground. On the southern hill slope are the burrows of Old Wheal Basset, which extend down to the valley floor (11).

The view of Tywarnhayle from Wheal Ellen reveals several tracks criss-crossing the hillside, of older origin than the level course of the tramways leading to the Elmore plant. The course of the steep incline which brought the ore from the upper portal down to the north end of the Elmore tramway is, however, no longer visible.

---

(11) Old Wheal Basset worked intermittently between 1854 and 1867 and produced 200 tons of copper ore but according to Hamilton Jenkin had been worked in the 1830s in conjunction with Wheal Ellen and Wheal Music. Delineation of the sett boundaries and their many changes is impossible today.

Wheal Ellen 70-inch engine house photographed in 1987. Up on the left is John's 70-inch engine house, and the ruins of the Elmore plant can be glimpsed to the right in the middle distance.

The Basset Mines

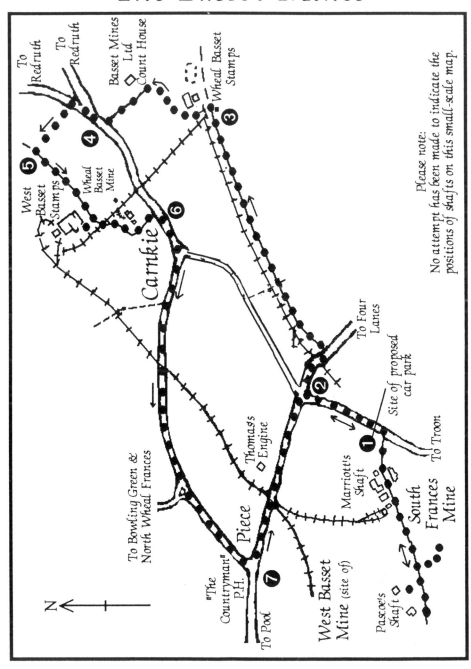

Please note:
No attempt has been made to indicate the positions of shafts on this small-scale map.

To Redruth
To Redruth

Basset Mines Ltd Court House

Wheal Basset Stamps

③

④

West Basset Stamps

⑤

Wheal Basset Mine

⑥

Carnkie

To Four Lanes

Site of proposed car park

②

①

To Troon

Thomas's Engine

Marriott's Shaft

South Frances Mine

To Bowling Green & North Wheal Frances

Piece

"The Countryman" P.H.

⑦

West Basset Mine (site of)

Pascoe's Shaft

To Pool

N

THE BASSET MINES

The tour of the main relics of Basset Mines involves only a short walk (about two-and-a-half miles), mostly on paths, tracks and minor roads; part of the route suggested uses a road which is often quite busy, but this can be avoided if you prefer, by taking a slightly shorter route. (See also the italicised note at the end about a new footpath which will cut out the worst of the road walking.) There are two pubs on the full route (just one on the shorter version), both of which serve food. You could also buy provisions at the post office / general store in Carnkie. Despite the small area covered, however, you need to allow at least three hours for the visit, because there is an exceptionally large amount to see. Go on a clear day if possible: the long views west, north and east hold a wealth of interest for the mining enthusiast. The surviving buildings and other surface remains of the Basset mines themselves and the neighbouring mines to the west cannot be matched anywhere in the world as a historic mining landscape, and if we had to pick a "walkabout" from this book as the ideal choice for a visitor with only one day available, this would undoubtedly be it. A recent report by the Cornwall Archaeological Unit declared, "It is only in the landscape between Carnkie and Piece that one can truly grasp the scale and extent of a large and successful 19th century mine." At the time of writing, shaft capping, building stabilisation and treatment of contaminated land are in progress. The work is being carried out jointly by Kerrier District Council and Groundwork Kerrier in close consultation with local residents via the Great Flat Lode Working Party, on which are represented all interested parties including the six small settlements in the area. The aim of this Working Party is to ensure that the essential character of the area is retained.

LOCATION   In and around the village of Carnkie on the south side of Carn Brea, about 2 miles south-west of Redruth. (Not to be confused with the other village of the same name in Wendron parish.) Grid reference for parking place (Marriott's Shaft): SW 682 394. OS maps: Pathfinder (1:25,000): Nos. 1359 & 1365. Landranger (1: 50,000): No. 203.

HOW TO GET THERE By car: Marriott's is probably found most easily by approaching it from Four Lanes, which is on the Redruth-Helston road (B3297). From the crossroads there, take the road heading north-west towards Pool and Camborne. After about a mile (i.e. shortly before you would reach the Countryman pub at Piece) there is a staggered crossroads; turn left there. Soon you will see an impressive group of mine buildings on your right, and these are the start-and-end point of this visit. At the time of writing, shaft capping and stabilising work on the buildings were being carried out on this site, and the plans include a car park for visitors which should be in place by the time this book is published. Currently there is limited parking on waste ground adjoining the mine buildings, but this will no longer be available once the new car park exists.

By public transport: There are bus services linking Camborne and Redruth with Carnkie and Piece: see current timetables. Probably the best plan would be to alight at the Countryman and pick up the directions at point 7.

THE BASSET MINES

The name "Basset" refers, of course, to the great landowning family whose seat was Tehidy. Mining in this area dates back a long way: the historian Tonkin, writing in about 1720, referred to "Carnkye, a tin work chiefly pertaining to the Basset's, out of which they have raised above £100,000 worth of tinn to no small profit of the adventurers, and that family." The mines with which we are concerned in this tour started as shallow copper workings in the late 18th / early 19th century. By the 1830s mergers resulted in fewer, larger mines which soon adopted steam power in order to go deeper. During the 1850s they began producing tin, which gradually increased to the point of superseding copper completely by about 1880. Three mines are included on this tour: South Wheal Frances (Frances, Baroness Basset, was the wife of the first Lord de Dunstanville), whose Marriott's Shaft is our starting point; West Wheal Basset, the immediate neighbour to the north; and Wheal Basset in the east, around Carnkie village. Prompted by boundary disputes, two successive mergers finally brought the three mines together in 1896 as Basset Mines Limited, ridding them finally of the shortcomings of the old cost-book companies. Sadly, owing to falling grade and falling price of tin the venture came to an end in December 1918. The ruins we see on the tour date from both before and after the 1896 merger. All three mines intersected a rich ore body at depth, called "The Great Flat Lode" because of its shallow angle of dip. Large areas of this below and to the east and west of the mines on our tour still remain unwrought.

Note: for the sake of brevity, in the account of the visit to these mines we have omitted the word "Wheal" when referring to West Wheal Basset and South Wheal Frances.

---

1 First of all, there is a great deal to explore at Marriott's Shaft, which was formerly part of South Frances. A fire which destroyed the 80-inch pumping engine at the time of the merger prompted the company to re-equip the shaft completely, with the intention to develop the Great Flat Lode in depth. The shaft itself lies roughly in the centre of the buildings complex - a superb example of "modern mining come to Cornwall" around the year 1900. The first building on your right as you pass through the gate housed a splendid 2-cylinder compound horizontal winding engine with a conical drum 12-25 ft in diameter which faced the shaft directly (1).

---

(1) The conical winding drum, commonly used at collieries but extremely rare in the West Country, was intended to speed up hoisting by the rope coiling on to or paying off from a larger diameter in the middle of the wind, once the engine had attained its full speed. The engine at Marriott's was built locally by Holman Brothers of Camborne - the only one of the

Marriott's Shaft collar about 1975, prior to capping.

All the buildings to the right of the track date from 1898-1900 but the massive structure on the left came a few years later. It was principally for miners' accommodation - a modernised version of the time-honoured miners' "dry" or changing house - but it may also have included a workshop and storage. The building represents very late use of masonry for a mine building, timber or sheet-steel-clad structures being more usual after the turn of the century.

Reverting to the right side of the path, note the use of modern, locked coil steel winding rope to form a low fence. Next to the winding engine a wall with six arches is the front of the boiler house, which, unusually for Cornwall, provided a common steam supply to all the engines (2). The chimney at the west end adjoins the impressive pumping-engine house; it was formerly much taller.

The pumping-engine house is the tallest building in the complex. The shaft (3) is immediately in front of it. In recent years it was covered by an ugly

---

three large steam engines here to have been made in Cornwall. Its cylinder diameters were 23 in high pressure and 43 in low pressure by 5 ft 6 in stroke. As built the exhaust was passed to a condenser, but this proved troublesome and it was altered to exhaust to atmosphere.

(2) When the shaft was first re-equipped it was thought that four boilers of the twin-furnace Lancashire type would suffice. After one exploded, however, two more were added. The explosion is assumed to have resulted partly from their having to be "forced" to produce enough steam.

(3) Marriott's Shaft attained a final depth of 340 fathoms vertically, a long way short of the

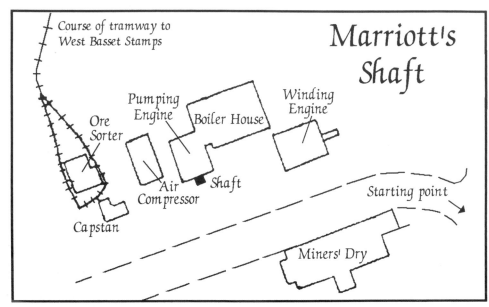

Marriott's Shaft

Course of tramway to West Basset Stamps

Ore Sorter

Pumping Engine

Boiler House

Winding Engine

Air Compressor

Shaft

Capstan

Starting point

Miners' Dry

concrete slab; perhaps one day money will be available for its replacement by a cap low down in the shaft throat to expose the handsome circular masonry-and-brick collar. A massive timber headframe, with an elevated ore-loading station and gantry, stood over the shaft, some of the concrete "feet" of which are still visible.

The pumping engine **(4)** was unconventional, only three or four other

5,000ft envisaged when the machinery was planned. Designed by Nicholas Trestrail, it provided for two sets of pumps, a double skip road, a capstan compartment and a ladderway for maintenance. In the event only one pumping compartment was used because only one pumping engine was installed instead of the two intended. The shaft is 16 ft diameter for the top 70 fm and 14 ft square below that. The pitwork with 18 in plungers was of Davey design along with the engine, the plungers being in line with the pump rod instead of offset Cornish fashion.

(4) The designer was Henry Davey of Leeds, better known for his horizontal differential pumping engines which were commonly used at collieries, both at surface and underground. The Basset engine had compounded inverted vertical cylinders of 40 and 80 in diameter with the piston rods connected to a wrought-iron beam beneath the floor. The cylinders stood at opposite ends of the house, the beam fulcrum being midway between them so that the stroke of the high pressure piston was 9 ft while that of the low pressure was 10 ft. The high pressure cylinder stood at the front and the beam beneath was extended out through the arched opening at low level, giving a stroke of 13 ft to the pump rod in the shaft. Possibly to placate local interests, the low-pressure cylinder at least was Cornish, being secondhand from the engine in the fire. The engine's air pump was outside the house at the left-hand (west) side - its mountings are still visible. The engine cost £7,500 new - a substantial sum for the time - and though the designer claimed it would do eleven strokes a minute, it never actually exceeded six-and-a-quarter. The late Luther Martin (who drove Pascoe's whim) saw the engine at work and said it used to "drop out of doors". It was also heavy on fuel - indeed it used to be said of Basset Mines that they consumed as much coal as the whole of Truro!

The buildings at Marriott's under construction, about 1897 ......

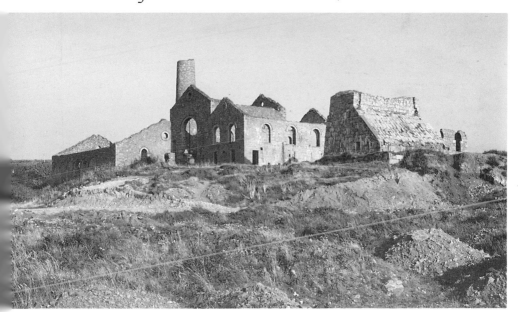

...... and as they are now

Basset Mines loco standing beside the whim at Marriott's, about 1910

A Trevithick Society visit to Marriott's, August 1983.
On the right is the Reidler compressor; further away are the remains of
Thomas's 60-inch engine on West Basset and the Carn Brea monument.

examples having been erected anywhere in the world. It stood in the left side of the house as you look across from the shaft to the massive arched opening in the front wall. To gain an idea of the level of the driver's floor, walk round to the rear of the house and the remains of a flight of steps finishing at floor level may still be seen.

Next to the pumping engine on the west is a lower house which contained a Reidler air-compressor **(5)** for supplying underground rock drills. The prominent openings low down in the walls of the house are bolt tunnels through which a man had to crawl when installing the foundation bolts of the engine. As these are no longer in place, some unlucky soul must have done likewise to free them when the engine was scrapped! Remains of a masonry loading between the compressor and the pump house mark the site of the pumping engine's air pump, which was worked by an auxiliary beam passing through a slot in the wall.

The last structure in the row is a small engine house which contained a worm-geared steam capstan for heavy lifts in the shaft, such as when installing the pumps and pump-rods. When not thus engaged the drum could be declutched and the engine used to drive the jaw crusher mentioned below, using a belt drive. Just to the north of the engine house is a tall, strange-looking structure with two prominent sloping faces. This is the core of a former ore sorter, the timber outside walls of which have either rotted or been removed. At the top of the structure was a "grizzly screen" composed of slanting steel rails with small gaps in between. Ore arriving from the shaft in man-wagons along a high-level gantry was tipped on to it - stuff small enough to pass through the gaps fell down the slope into a hopper on the west face, while larger stones fell down the east slope to a jaw crusher whose mountings can be seen. This reduced them to the smaller size. In both cases, the stone was delivered via hopper doors into wagons on the mine's tramway, which had tracks on both sides of the structure. The tramway was worked by a steam locomotive built in Germany, which hauled the wagons from here to one of the two sets of stamps and dressing floors the mine possessed. (These are both visited later on this tour.) Owing to the removal of the large dumps and tramway embankment in recent years, the latter's course is a little hard to follow. We shall, however, encounter it in places as the walk proceeds.

The view westward from the ore hopper and capstan area is very striking. It represents the last of the great Cornish mining landscapes still recognisable as such - indeed it is possible to find positions in the shallow valley from which 17 engine houses may be counted, if we include those behind us.

The two closest are at Pascoe's Shaft, also part of South Frances: 80-inch pumping engine on the right, 36-inch whim a little further away. They

---

(5) This was a cross-compound, Corliss valve horizontal engine whose two-stage air cylinders were in tandem with the steam cylinders. It was built by Frazer & Chalmers, of Erith, Kent, who supplied such engines all over the world. The mounting blocks for this engine are still intact, as is the central pit for the flywheel and the condenser, but it is understood that after the current stabilisation work internal access is to be discouraged!

date from about 1887. On the skyline ahead is the Grenville housing estate at Troon, and to the right of that are two engine houses belonging to South Condurrow Mine; again, the nearer one held a pumping engine and the other was for winding. Closer at hand in roughly the same direction are two engine houses facing one another at Fortescue's Shaft, Grenville United Mine. The first structures to be restored under the Mineral Tramways Project, they comprise whim (left) and 90-inch pumping engine (right). Both date from 1881. To the left of them, and closer to us, is the 30-inch whim-engine house at Daubuz's Shaft, South Frances, which stands with its back to us at the western limit of Basset Mines. It also worked pumps in Daubuz' Shaft via a short run of flat-rods. Left of that and further away is the New Stamps house of Grenville United. Now going right, just left of Pascoe's whim and further off, in a slight depression, is the one remaining engine house of West Frances, a small whim. Everything else on that mine has disappeared.

Further off still, in the same direction, is the group of buildings at King Edward Mine, now used by students at the Camborne School of Mines (6). On the skyline in roughly the same direction as Pascoe's pumping-engine house is the big 80-inch pumping-engine house at Neame's Shaft, Condurrow United. Much further right, to the north of Marriott's and between where we are standing and the nearby hamlet of Piece, today's green fields mark the site of West Basset. Of the shafts, buildings, dressing floors and burrows of this once extensive mine, scarcely anything visible remains except the gaunt bob wall of a 60-inch pumping engine at Thomas's Shaft, in the extreme east of the sett. To see it, look towards the Carn Brea monument. We can inspect it more closely later in this walkabout.

The ground on which the mine stood was too flat for efficient ore-dressing, so in the 1870s the dressing floors were moved nearly a mile east to a site which then came to be known as West Basset Stamps, on the slopes of Carn Brea overlooking Carnkie village. This, too, will be visited later. Ore from Marriott's Shaft was also sent there for processing after the merger, but the removal of burrows in recent years has obscured the course of the tramway to the stamps.

Before leaving this viewpoint, a patch of dense scrub will be noted on your left, on the edge of the fields on the other side of the track. A steam whim formerly stood here, arranged so that it could haul from both Marriott's and Pascoe's Shafts. It was here that wire rope was first introduced into Cornwall in 1857. It quickly superseded hemp ropes and chains, which had been used previously. The whim engine had a set of stamps attached to it to deal with the tin being discovered in South Frances, and ultimately drove stamps only, the waste from which created the now overgrown burrow.

---

(6) Visits by organised parties are possible, both underground and also to the fine and still growing collection of mining machinery housed in the surface buildings. Plans to open it to the public are in hand: Phase 1 (Easter 1995 if possible) would be the ore-dressing plant and museum; Phase 2 the underground visit.

A small detour to inspect the whim / stamps engine site and Pascoe's pumping-engine house is recommended. For this, *rejoin the main track passing between the buildings on your left and follow it westwards until a capped shaft marker is seen on the left. Turn towards it* - it is inscribed as an unnamed shaft and probably enabled the whim / stamps engine to draw dressing water from the adit. *From it turn half-left into the copse* and the lower part of the rear end side wall of the engine house will be seen, along with a large bank of cinders. The ruins are orientated towards Marriott's Shaft. The stamps stood on the south side of the engine, and on the level area in front were a few buddles to treat the stuff coming from the stamps.

To reach Pascoe's pumping engine, return to the main track and cross over it - at the time of writing the arrangement of paths in this area is a little indefinite. The authors understand that when the shaft in front of the house has been capped, access down steps to the bottom of the plug doorway opening will be possible, to give an impressive view of the bob wall overhead. (7)

Pascoe's Shaft is very close to the boundary with West Frances mine to the north. Today it is hard to imagine the paraphernalia of the latter's dressing floors which covered the fields right down to the present hedge boundary.

The house of Pascoe's whim to the west is also accessible and quite well preserved. This engine had a 30-inch cylinder (not 36-inch as sometimes stated) and the boiler house is large enough for two Cornish boilers.

Now to start the walk to Basset and West Basset Stamps return along the main track to the road (Filtrick Lane) and turn left. The house on the right was the count house of South Frances until that mine became part of Basset Mines Ltd in 1896; after that it was the home of the engineer, one William Jelbert. The tramway also linked South Frances with the dressing floors at Wheal Basset on the south side of Carnkie; the first part of this walk will follow quite closely the route of that part of the tramway (8). Notice that at one point the road suddenly narrows. The reason is that a whim-engine house used to stand here: the remains of it can still be discerned beside the road on the right. It hauled from a shaft over in the

---

(7) The engine here was an 80-inch one built by the St Austell Foundry - its largest ever - in 1881 for Old Shepherds lead mine near Newlyn East. It was moved here secondhand in 1887, using steam road haulage. In 1916, with the engine then drawing from a depth of 340 fathoms diagonally, the main cap at the top of the piston rod broke without warning. The piston descended under steam with such force that nearly the whole engine was wrecked. The driver managed to reach one of the projecting bob-plats over the shaft to avoid the scalding steam in the house, from where he was rescued by fire-escape ladder, shaken but unhurt. The main parts of the engine were replaced by a firm called Worsley Mesnes of Wigan and erected using the original beam - arguably the last Cornish beam engine ever built - and this worked for two years down to the 1918 closure. Note the unusual "slit window" architecture of the house. A few such houses were built in the 1880s, in the belief that extra strength was gained.

(8) The Wheal Basset Tramway was horse-hauled until about 1906, and ran from the stamps at the east end of the sett almost as far as the Four Lanes road, to a shaft called Samson's. There were sidings to several other shafts. In 1906 or a little later the line was extended to Marriott's Shaft, South Frances, and a steam locomotive came into use.

fields to the east and was later adapted to haul from Marriott's Shaft in the opposite direction by using bevel gearing to realign the winding drum. The tramway crossed the road about here and ran through what is now a very overgrown area on the right; it represents an early example of a mine clean-up operation. The precise course of this part of the tramway linking with Marriott's Shaft thus became obscured. Across the field in front of you as you reach the crossroads is one of two shafts in this area called

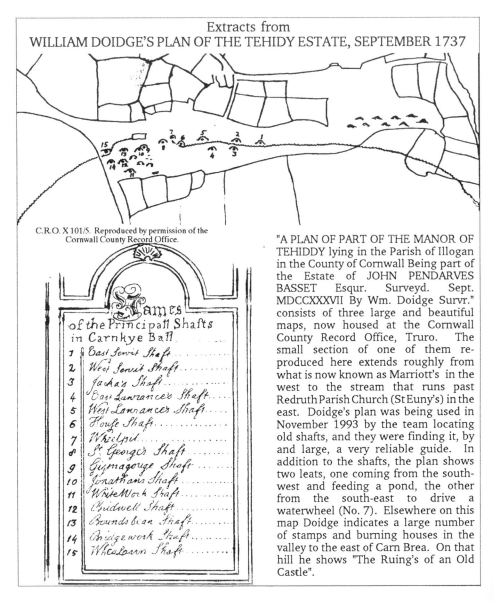

Extracts from
WILLIAM DOIDGE'S PLAN OF THE TEHIDY ESTATE, SEPTEMBER 1737

C.R.O. X 101/5. Reproduced by permission of the
Cornwall County Record Office.

Names
of the Principall Shafts
in Carnkye Ball.

1. East Servit Shaft
2. West Servit Shaft
3. Jacka's Shaft
4. East Lawrance's Shaft
5. West Lawrance's Shaft
6. House Shaft
7. Wheelpit
8. St George's Shaft
9. Gizmagouge Shaft
10. Jonathans Shaft
11. WhiteWork Shaft
12. Bridwell Shaft
13. Boundsbean Shaft
14. Bridgework Shaft
15. Wheelawn Shaft

"A PLAN OF PART OF THE MANOR OF TEHIDDY lying in the Parish of Illogan in the County of Cornwall Being part of the Estate of JOHN PENDARVES BASSET Esqur. Surveyd. Sept. MDCCXXXVII By Wm. Doidge Survr." consists of three large and beautiful maps, now housed at the Cornwall County Record Office, Truro. The small section of one of them reproduced here extends roughly from what is now known as Marriott's in the west to the stream that runs past Redruth Parish Church (St Euny's) in the east. Doidge's plan was being used in November 1993 by the team locating old shafts, and they were finding it, by and large, a very reliable guide. In addition to the shafts, the plan shows two leats, one coming from the southwest and feeding a pond, the other from the south-east to drive a waterwheel (No. 7). Elsewhere on this map Doidge indicates a large number of stamps and burning houses in the valley to the east of Carn Brea. On that hill he shows "The Ruing's of an Old Castle".

Carnkie. The low burrow running away to the left of it carried a rail track which linked with the branch of the tramway serving West Basset Stamps.

2 *At the staggered crossroads, turn right.* Please keep to the verge on the right at first: the traffic along here tends to be fast. Soon you pass a road-junction sign. A few yards beyond that, the mineral tramway to Wheal Basset Stamps passed under the road in a short tunnel, and although road widening and dumping in recent years, together with the thick growth of vegetation, have obscured much of the evidence, the cutting where the line ran is still clearly visible on the right. The tunnel portal still survives on this side of the road. **(9)**

Cross the road now, with care, and take the footpath on the left, which after about twenty yards joins a wider track heading north-east. It runs very close to but mostly at a slightly higher level than the course of the tramway, which lies buried under the tips on your left. Old maps such as the one made by William Doidge in 1737 (part of which is reproduced in this book) reveal numerous shafts, most of them quite close to the track on the left-hand side. Ignore the track which crosses and leads down on the left towards Carnkie, but soon after that, where the main track bends a little to the right and rises slightly, you could continue ahead for a few paces to look at the site of Richards' Shaft. Both engine house and shaft have now vanished, and the site has been turned into a smooth slope, but on the left is a cindery bank which gives some idea of the amount of coal burnt by the engines here. The view north and east from here is good, but a little later it is even better, so it seems best to delay a description till then. Return to the upper track and continue as before, heading towards a tall, ruined stack. A short way further along, the mineral railway ran in a shallow cutting on the left, and its route becomes very clear as it goes on from there to the Wheal Basset stamps and dressing floors, passing very close to other shafts (Roberts' and Theager's) en route. A recent archaeological survey has revealed that cobbled copper-spalling floors have survived on both sides of the track in the area between Roberts' and Theager's (or Theaker's) Shafts. In 1865, Spargo noted that the mine's 357 employees included 46 women and 63 boys; many of them must have worked on such cobbled floors, perhaps under the shelter of flimsy buildings, now gone without trace.

Across the valley to your left are the remarkably complete ruins of the West Basset stamps complex, to be visited later. In front of you are the comparatively incomplete remains of Wheal Basset Stamps. Some maps refer to these as East Basset Stamps but they are not so named by mining historians. Moreover, in the authors' view, the name is misleading because East Wheal Basset was a mine in its own right, with its own set of steam stamps. It stood on the slope behind the filling station distantly visible in the east.

The whole area around the Wheal Basset Stamps was subjected to an ill-

---

(9) It is hoped that as part of the Mineral Tramways Project the entire course of the Basset tramway, from Marriott's to Wheal Basset Stamps, will be opened up as a path, including the tunnel under the road.

thought-out scheme in the 1970s when the dumps were removed for reprocessing and shafts filled, leaving a sterile area rich in mineral salts on which scarcely anything will grow, although the heather and thrift are making a brave attempt.

As the track reaches the building ruins you pass the foundations of a small haulage engine and the aforementioned stack on your right. The engine hauled wagons of ore up an incline from Lyle's Shaft, whose ivy-clad pumping-engine house can be seen down in the bottom of the valley. (We shall be visiting that area later.) The stamps-engine house is on the left of the track - its boilers stood behind but their site is totally buried, the track in fact passing over it. They were served by the stack on the right.

The concrete work on the engine house and in front of it dates from 1938 when dressing equipment was erected to reprocess the burrows. The house was used as an ore bin and in front Californian stamps stood where previously the engines' crankshafts and flywheels had been. An opening at the rear gives a good interior view of the house which was unusual in having two 30-inch-cylinder rotary beam engines side-by-side. That they were double-acting engines is proved by the slots in the bob wall for the trunnion-bearing retaining bolts. By 1895 these two engines drove 96 heads of Cornish stamps which stood in two rows, one on each side. The racket they kicked up must have been appalling, though the saying is that people in Carnkie noticed them only when they were not working!

The track continuing north-eastwards from Wheal Basset Stamps is thought to have been an extension of the Redruth and Chasewater Railway's Wheal Buller branch at one period, though firm evidence for this seems to be lacking.

From that track at the eastern end of the site there is a remarkable view to the east and north. Close by and almost straight ahead are the remains of a mine pond. The two chimney stacks down in the valley beyond that were part of the big Seleggan smelting works **(10)**. Just to the left of the distant filling station is, as mentioned earlier, the site of East Wheal Basset, and the rough patch further left again marks the site of Louisa's Shaft, North Buller Mine. Then come the two prominent engine houses of Wheal Uny (Hine's 70-inch pumping left, 25-inch whim right), standing on the high ground above Redruth parish church and Carn Brea village; these are due to be consolidated shortly. Cutting off the view of the sea horizon to the right is St Agnes Beacon. Further left is Carn Brea hill, with Carnkie village nestling below, towards which we now make our way.

3 *Walk down the steepish slope on the SW side of the mine buildings.*

A detour (right) into the Frue vanner house just below the stamps engine reveals the concrete bases of classifiers and separators installed in 1938 to

---

(10) The Cornish Tin Smelting Co. Ltd began operations here in 1887; it was the largest active smelting works in Cornwall during the 20th century, and the last one to survive. It closed in 1931. A photograph of it when working is in Barton's *A History of Tin Mining and Smelting in Cornwall.* The Cornwall Archaeological Unit has carried out a trial dig on the site and discovered many foundations. There are plans to put a small car park on part of the site to serve the eastern end of the Great Flat Lode.

Wheal Basset Stamps: the remains of the building that housed two 30-inch rotary beam engines which eventually drove 96 heads of stamps

Wheal Basset Stamps: interior of Frue Vanner House

treat the burrows. The vanners for which this impressive structure was built were introduced early this century to improve the ore-concentration process **(11)**. From the vanner house can be seen the datestone inscribed "WB 1868" on the bob wall of the stamps engine house. ("WB"=Wheal Basset.)

After a few yards follow the path (if that's not too grand a word) which runs gently downhill beneath the vanner house. The path in question (which if current plans are fulfilled will quite soon be replaced by a zigzag path) heads roughly towards the smelting works stacks and passes between the remains of two quite tall retaining walls. These are the best remaining evidence of the fact that this slope was, when the mines were active, a series of terraces on which were the buddles, round frames, settling tanks and other features typical of dressing floors. They were driven by a horizontal engine whose site is indeterminate. The upper wall is close to collapse and will probably have to be buried to ensure its survival. The square building and stack on the slope north-east of the vanner house are thought to have been associated with an arsenic calciner, but there is no sign of a labyrinth collector flue.

Bear left down a stony track, which soon becomes a tarmacked driveway and passes beside the former count house of Basset Mines Ltd. This was till quite recently in use as a restaurant, and we understand that it will soon resume this rôle.

4 *At the road, turn right, then almost immediately bear left, and after about 25 yards turn left on to a path# which begins at a gap to the right of a wooden gate. (Please note: although this path appears to be in regular use it is not a right of way, and it may be necessary to approach the West Basset Stamps complex by means of the road into Carnkie village, turning right at point 6 on the sketch map.)*

At the bottom of the dip look left and you will see on higher ground the scanty remains of the house of a 2-cylinder horizontal winding engine and its boiler-house stack. The engine was intended to haul from Miner's Shaft, now hidden amongst the gorse nearer the path, but was in fact adapted to haul from Lyle's Shaft in the opposite direction, that is, to the west. An air compressor serving Lyle's Shaft was installed next to the winding engine.

Continue along the path uphill, cross the wider track and carry on, passing through a gap in a barbed-wire fence. When you come to an open area (probably the site of a mine pond), take the path at the top right-hand corner, which still goes on uphill for a few more yards.

5 *On reaching a second wider track, turn left. This soon brings you to the magnificent remains of West Basset Stamps, on your right. To appreciate this complex to the full, it is best to continue past it to the far (west) end,*

---

(11) The vanner house was built on a site that had been occupied by a covered area of buddles and settling tanks since the great expansion of Wheal Basset's dressing floors in 1868. Each vanner consisted of a slowly moving endless india-rubber belt, on the top surface of which the pulp leaving the stamps was placed. The belt was washed with a stream of water and also given an agitation which helped to separate the lighter fractions from the tin concentrate - the forerunner of the Holman or James table still used today.

Stamps Engine
Stamps Engine Stack
Boiler House

Course of Tramway from West Basset Mine & Marriott's Shaft

West Basset Stamps

Calciner Stack

Vanner House

Vanner Engine

Direction of Walk

Calciner

Buddles & Slimes Treatment

Course of Tramway to/ from Wheal Basset Stamps

N

Direction of Walk

Pumping Engine

Small Beam Engine

Remnant of Miners' Dry

Chimney stack

Wheal Basset Count House

Lyle's Shaft

Stonebreaker
(probable site of)

Beam Whim (Capstan Engine)

Course of Tramway to/ from Wheal Basset Stamps

Boiler Houses

Wheal Basset

Remnant of Smithy

Direction of Walk

Carnkie Village

West Basset Stamps, August 1987: the ruins of the vanner house, with the
stamps-engine house and calciner stack behind

West Basset Stamps, 26th October 1991: Kenneth describing those same
buildings, with a convex buddle for his platform

turn right along a rudimentary path and enter the building by the second doorway on the right. **(12)** *Take great care as drainage channels lie in the floor, hidden by undergrowth.*

The large building you are now standing in contains a number of circular concrete buddles: seven convex, seven concave and two smaller "dumb buddles". The buddles are explained in footnote 12. The ore was brought in along two tramways: one which crossed the fields to the left came from Thomas's and Marriott's Shafts, and the other was from Lyle's Shaft, a short way below the stamps site. Traces of revetted embankments, cuttings and short tunnels marking the courses of these tramroads have survived in the area around the tall engine house at the highest point of the complex, which contained the beam engine that drove the stamps **(13)**. **PLEASE NOTE: We do NOT recommend that you try climbing up to the stamps engine until it is consolidated and made safe.** In this century its crankshaft foundation needed concrete strengthening to withstand the years of pounding and vibration. Bases of handrail stanchions around them reveal that safety of personnel was starting to be taken seriously. There were 80 heads of Cornish stamps in the final installation, 32 on one side and 48 on the other.

From the stamps the ore was passed to the Frue vanner house just below them, a smaller version of what we saw earlier, and the best-preserved example in Cornwall. Square openings for chutes conveying ore material from the stamps can be seen in the north wall. The projecting part of the house contained a small steam engine which drove the vanners. From there the pulp (as the pulverised ore and water mixture was termed) was wheeled to the buddles **(14)**. Note the signs of alterations and extensions to the building you are in, and the poor quality of the stonework in the walls, an indication of turn-of-the-century work.

The structure on the left (west) side housed twin Brunton calciners, where

---

(12) The first door gave access to a small building thought to have been the tin store, the only lock-up on the place. It did not need to be big as tin ore averaged only 1 -1.5% of the rock which had to be processed. This helps to account for the large waste tips at long-lived mines.

(13) The engine here was built by the Tuckingmill Foundry, Camborne, in 1875. It had a 40-inch cylinder and, unusually for Cornwall, had cam-driven valve gear. An auxiliary beam at the rear worked pumps in a shallow shaft to draw water for dressing purposes. Later on, water came from Thomas's 60-inch engine via a leat running alongside the tramway, traces of which remain. The 1878 and 1906 OS maps show five mine ponds immediately above the stamps-engine house.

(14) By this time the pulp was composed mainly of fines, being little more than a sludge. It was mixed with more water in the small "dumb buddles", shallow bowl-like pits. The sludge was poured in at the centre; the coarser, heavier particles settled near the centre, the finer ones nearer the edges. This process was known as "classifying". The water was then drained off and the ore was dug out and barrowed according to size to the convex or concave buddles, where it was washed and brushed by bristles carried on rotating arms. This action removed most of the waste material, leaving the heavy material, the tin oxide, behind. The waste washwater could be reprocessed, each time seeing a greater concentration of tin particles. The concave buddles were generally reserved for the finest material of all. This dressing system had the drawback of being "batch processing": more modern equipment enables this process to be continuous.

the ore was roasted to drive off the arsenic. The labyrinth where arsenic was recovered - if there ever was one - has disappeared but the chimney stack still stands, in remarkably good condition, a little to the north. Remains of buddles in the undergrowth to the west of the ruins show that the complex extended beyond the present walls in the mine's last days. The plant also extended both to the east of the vanner house and to the south of the present path, where there were batteries of settling tanks, rag (or rack) frames and round frames; evidence of many of these features still exists under the vegetation. Drive to this complex was by a waterwheel whose site has totally vanished; it stood to the east.

From West Basset Stamps, return to and continue along the same track, which bears left and then right, affording a front view of Lyle's 80-inch pumping-engine house **(15)**. The shaft is directly in front. The beam whim which occupied the smaller engine house to the right was superseded in later days by the more modern engine on Miner's Shaft. A row of tall pulley stands supporting the rope between this engine and the shaft is prominent in photographs of the mine at work. The beam whim was retained for capstan work in the shaft, having an auxiliary winding drum geared from the crankshaft. Its mountings may still be seen, if not obscured by a parked vehicle! The first photograph opposite shows the arrangement well; a dozen-or-so pictures in the late J.H.Trounson's *Mining in Cornwall,* Vol. 1, also depict Basset mines in their working days. The common boiler house which supplied steam to both engines stood between them, the roof line on the side of the pumping-engine house having only recently disappeared under the ivy. Part of a second boiler house on the east side of the house is still visible. On the opposite side, to the right of the track, the former (North) Wheal Basset count house is still lived in. Between it and the track stand a few crumbling walls of the miners' dry.

Following the path around the whim-engine house, which has a tree growing inside it, one sees on the right a ruin which is part of the mine's smithy. The carpenters' shop stood slightly further west. A little to the east of Lyle's Shaft a tiny beam-engine house, almost like a miniature, is believed to have housed a small engine for supplying or recirculating water to the mine's dressing floors. Contemporary maps, however, show a large stonebreaker beside it. The purpose of the lone stack standing nearby has not definitely been established.

Now continue along the track between the houses to join the road in Carnkie village, opposite the Wheal Basset Inn. (The last syllable of the village's name, by the way, is pronounced to rhyme with "tie", and derives from the Cornish word *ky,* a dog.)

6 *Turn right.* (When you reach the Methodist Church, to shorten the walk somewhat and avoid the busiest stretch of road on the route you could turn left. After nearly half a mile, this will bring you back to the staggered

---

(15) Lyle's engine was erected about 1880 - the third engine to stand on this shaft, which belonged to North Wheal Basset until that mine was wound up in 1872, and was taken over by Wheal Basset in 1878. It is on record that four engine houses in the district were demolished to provide enough stone for Lyle's pumping engine and whim.

Lyle's 80-inch pumping engine at work, early 20th century. The house for the old beam whim engine is on the right, just out of view. (Other details in this scene are described in the text on the opposite page.)

The same scene about 20 years ago. The roof-line of the big boiler house is visible on the pumping-engine house, but has since become obscured by ivy.

crossroads referred to at the start of point 2. To return to Marriott's, go a few yards right, then left.) *For the full suggested route, continue ahead through the village.* Hidden behind the houses on the left just beyond the road junction is Grace's Shaft, to which ran flat-rods from at least one of Lyle's engines. An engine-house ruin here was one of those whose stone was re-used at Lyle's in 1880. After passing the rather impressive farmhouse at Carnkie Farm you are out in the country, but the fields on the right were once covered with the buildings and burrows of a small neighbouring mine, North Wheal Frances.

7 Eventually you will reach the little hamlet of Piece. A. K. Hamilton Jenkin suggests that this unusual name derives from an old mine called "The Washells Called the Piece". Who or what "Washells" are or were is anyone's guess; could it be a corruption of "wastrel", the term used in Cornwall for unenclosed land where tinners were free to prospect? *Just this side of the Countryman pub, take the sharp-left turning, the rather busy road linking Pool with Four Lanes. Again, please take great care as you walk.* The school bears the initials ISB, meaning "Illogan School Board" - a reminder of the fact that this area was part of Illogan parish until boundary changes were made in 1973. The building is perhaps a surprisingly large one for so out-of-the-way a place, but remember that School Boards existed only between 1870 and 1902, a period when mining was still very much alive and even expanding in this area.

As soon as you have passed the school, notice the remains of the foundations for a horizontal engine in the field on the opposite side: a relic of West Basset mine, though its precise function is doubtful. A little more than a hundred yards beyond the school, this road was crossed by the mineral tramway linking West Basset with its dressing floors in Carnkie. This is just before reaching the surviving bob wall of Thomas's engine, the eastern pumping unit of West Basset. The course of the tramway is fairly clear on the left immediately beyond a wooden gate, where earth has been heaped up beside the road quite recently, presumably to deter travellers or other drivers of vehicles from using the track. It still provides access for walkers to the engine house, however, and it is from behind that one of its most unusual features can be seen: the fact that the stack was inside the house. Thomas's 60-inch pumping engine was erected in 1854. This last fact is proclaimed on a date stone in the fine bob wall of dressed granite, which contrasts strongly with the blackish rubble used to construct the boiler-house wall adjoining it - though even that has strong granite quoins. **(16)** Between the road and the engine house an area has been devoted to

---

(16) Note the iron reinforcement applied to the bob wall in the engine's last years. Later bob walls generally had iron tie-rods built in, but long-lived engines without this feature commonly required bob-wall strengthening. Here the engine suffered a serious fire within months of the 1896 final merger. (West Basset and South Frances had joined forces in 1892.) It was suspected that both this and the fire at Marriott's were started deliberately. Thomas's engine was left with a bent piston-rod. From then on it was worked slowly for a period, delivering water to the West Basset dressing floors, underground work at West Basset having ceased. When the engine was scrapped, its beam was moved to Pascoe's Shaft where it went underground for use as a balance bob for the 80-inch engine.

small trial plots. Different treatments of the contaminated land are being compared in order to discover what conditions best enable the natural vegetation to re-establish itself.

Over to the right now you have a fine view of the buildings at Marriott's Shaft. To return to them, *take the first turning on the right.*

NOTE: A new footpath is to be opened up (and may in fact be available by the time this book is published) using the route of the West Basset tramway in order to make a direct link from Thomas's to Marriott's. This will clearly be far preferable to continuing along the road.

West Basset Mine: the ruins of Thomas's 60-inch pumping-engine house

5
DOLCOATH

The Queen of Cornish Mines is looking much less regal now than in her heyday, and what there is left to see has for many decades been eroded away by random mineral searching, new industry, new housing, fly tipping, vandalism and general neglect; but to leave Cornwall's greatest mine out of this book would have been unthinkable. And despite the unflattering picture just painted, the short stroll described here has much to recommend it even to those with little interest in industrial archaeology. Go on a clear day if possible, because there are some magnificent views, first across the Red River valley to the historic mining landscape on the north side of Carn Brea, and later of the coastline from St Agnes Beacon to St Ives. The climb to that second vantage point is not at all strenuous, and the going is easy throughout, although a little mild scrambling is needed here and there. The route, which cannot be much above a mile in length including the optional visit to Stray Park, passes through a surprisingly rural area as well as a few suburban streets and the derelict or semi-derelict land at the heart of the old mine. There has been much talk recently that the last of these is threatened by new housing developments which could destroy even more of the evidence of past glories than has already vanished. Nearly all the shafts, for example, have long since disappeared. Only limited areas around New Sump Shaft and the few surviving engine houses are likely to escape redevelopment in the long term. The engine houses themselves are due for conservation in 1995-6 under the Kerrier District Council's Derelict Land Programme, funded by Derelict Land Grants from Central Government, but with the current policy of burying what is loosely defined as "contaminated land", together with pressure for development, the long-term outlook for the rest of the mine looks bleak.

LOCATION Nearly a mile east of the centre of Camborne. Grid reference for parking place: SW 661 404. OS maps: Pathfinder (1:25,000): Nos. 1359 & 1365. Landranger (1:50,000): No. 203.

HOW TO GET THERE By car: Turn south from the A3047 (Camborne-Redruth road) at Chapel Road, on the east side of Tuckingmill. At the steeply sloping T-junction turn right (Dolcoath Road), and immediately beyond the engine house on the left there is space for several cars.

By public transport: There are fairly frequent bus services between Camborne and Redruth using the A3047. Alight at Tuckingmill, and either walk along Chapel Road and turn right as directed for car drivers, or if you are at Tuckingmill Church take Church View Road and turn left at the Dolcoath Road crossroads. This will bring you to the engine house which is the start-and-end point for the walkabout.

1 Start by inspecting the engine house, close by on your left **(1)**.

---

(1) The rotative beam engine here was multi-purpose. It hoisted from New East Shaft using a winding drum outside the near (west) front of the house. The shaft was somewhere in the

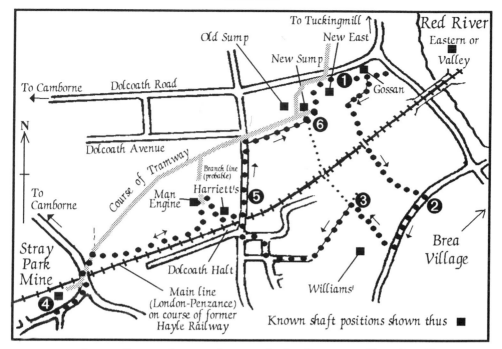

To start the walk, continue a few yards in the same direction (i.e. east, towards Carn Brea, dominated by the monument to Lord de Dunstanville of Basset, a prominent mine promoter), using the narrow track immediately on the right of the ruined buildings, and turn right (south) on the wide track# heading towards the nearest hill, Carn Entral.

Before going up the track, however, look left and you will see close to the road a stone cairn marking the site of Gossan Shaft. This is one of the lucky ones - most of Dolcoath's numerous shafts have totally vanished.

It is now worth walking a few more paces eastwards to get the full benefit of the view across the Red River valley. So much tipping and so-called landscaping has been done on both sides of the valley in recent years that it is hard to imagine the complex of ore-dressing sheds, stamps, calciners etc. that formerly adorned the valley slopes.

The active mine with the tall headgear half-left of us is Cook's Shaft of South Crofty mine, the main hoisting shaft of Cornwall's last mine to work.

waste ground to the west but is now totally obscured. By means of an auxiliary beam the engine also pumped water from adit level, via a shaft immediately behind the house, to supply Dolcoath's stamps and dressing floors. Two steam stamps occupied the area now covered by a bakery complex on the opposite side of the road. Indeed, the hump in the road is the site of a level crossing with the mine's 1ft 10 in gauge steam-worked tramway on the last leg of the ore's journey from the various shafts to the stamps. About 1894 the beam engine was replaced by a more modern steam winder, mentioned later, and the house became derelict. In 1913, however, it was converted to an electricity substation. Various excrescences were added, including the low building adjoining, but most of these are due for removal when the building is stabilised as part of the Mineral Tramways Project.

DOLCOATH MINE

Of all Cornish mines, Dolcoath was the deepest and most productive, and enjoyed the longest period of continuous working. Even today "as deep as Dolcoath" is a local expression for conveying the depth of a hole. Dolcoath also provides a classic instance of a rich copper mine gradually turning into a rich tin mine as the workings probed ever deeper into the hard granite: a characteristic of mines in this particular area.

In his description of Dolcoath the celebrated mining historian, the late Mr T.R.Harris, divided the mine's history into three phases: its shadowy beginnings; the spacious days of the cost-book company under which it became Cornwall's leading copper producer; and its final period as a tin mine under a limited liability company.

Of its initial phase there is little record, though recent shaft-capping operations uncovered some old stopes, once open to the sky, buried under many feet of mine debris. Dolcoath was paying dues to the Tehidy estate by 1731, at which time it was only one of seven setts which were later to merge. Newcomen-type atmospheric pumping engines were in use before 1758 - indeed, what was possibly the base of one was unearthed on Old Sump Shaft during recent capping. In 1781 came the first Boulton & Watt engine and twenty years later Richard Trevithick began experimenting with higher steam pressures in boilers and engines on the mine. This culminated in the setting to work in 1816 of the first true Cornish beam pumping engine, on New Sump Shaft. The so-called Red River valley which crosses the eastern end of the property provided a ready discharge for a system of adits to drain the upper levels of the mine, which also boasted an underground waterwheel at one stage. A deeper adit, coming to surface much further downstream at Roscroggan, came into use about 1800 and still serves South Crofty today.

The 19th century saw a gathering assemblage of steam power for pumping, hoisting, crushing and stamping as the workforce ran into four figures. The Stray Park sett to the west was acquired and in 1854 a man-engine was brought into use near the centre of the mine to convey miners to and from the deeper levels. A brave young lady who was allowed to use it about 1860 in defiance of local superstition achieved notoriety when she lost part of her dress which became entangled! In general the mine's safety record was good by Cornish standards. The most serious mishap occurred in 1893 when timbers known as the "great stull" supporting the roof of a large stope at the 412 fathom level gave way, killing seven miners. An eighth was rescued after 37 hours.

Electric pumps came into use in 1912, but nine years later the mine came to an end, creating a depression in the district from which it has never fully recovered, even today. The tragic and largely unnecessary destruction of surface features of Cornwall's greatest mine both before and after the Second World War has left us with little to remind us of an enterprise which did so much to foster technical developments in metal mining a century and more ago. Today's conservation plans are welcome - but too late!

New East Shaft, Dolcoath: workers including bal-maidens. This view is
looking north-east, with the North Stamps engine house in the distance.

Dolcoath miners armed with bunches of candles. On the left is the
Dolcoath Avenue compressor north of Harriett's Shaft. The mine tramway
here is heading east towards the tall headframe at Old Sump Shaft and
New Sump Shaft beyond. The stack furthest left is South Stamps.

East Pool
North whim, South whim, Old Kitty "70"
Roberts's 90-inch Wht Agar behind
behind

Tincroft North
stamps - Tyjo's
36-inch behind

Cam Brea
Highburrow
East / 90-inch

North Tincroft
crusher whim

South Tincroft
/ 70-inch

Old Cooks Kitchen
/ whim / 55-inch
pumping engine
(man-engine
stack behind)

Stamps engine

Dolcoath
Eastern
shaft or
Valley shaft

Dolcoath
Old smithy

Dolcoath
Californian
stamps

Dolcoath
Old stamps

Photo looking East across Red River Valley from bob plat of Dolcoath North stamps abt 1910.

90

The workings here now extend nearly 3,000 feet below the surface and reach the same horizon as the deepest workings of Dolcoath. The tall buildings left of the headgear house the mill where the tin ore can be concentrated ready for sending abroad to the smelter **(2)**.

Until the 1920s, twenty to thirty mine stacks could be counted on the far side of the valley, stretching away into the distance. See the photograph opposite. A similar one taken about 1905 appears in Tom Harris' book on Dolcoath. Beyond South Crofty lies the East Pool and Agar mine where two of the beam engines have been preserved by the National Trust. To the right can be seen the stumpy headgear of Robinson's Shaft, South Crofty, just peeping over a rusty building, while still further right stand the two ruined engine houses on Chapple's Shaft, Old Cook's Kitchen mine. The isolated stack of the pumping engine (of which we get the side view) looks odd because all the upper brickwork has fallen leaving the decorative masonry collar resembling a lid! Beyond these two can be seen two distant engine houses and a stack, relics of South Tincroft mine, its neighbour North Tincroft having completely vanished beneath a rash of superstores.

The river below has been streamed for tin, perhaps for many hundreds of years, but certainly since the early 19th century; little evidence of that fact remains along this particular section of it, but there are clear traces of leats on both sides further up the valley. On the near side can be seen the masonry remains of a wheelpit; at one time there were waterwheels working stamps and dressing machinery on both sides.

Dolcoath Mine extended a short distance beyond the river: the most easterly of its shafts (Eastern or Valley Shaft) and the site of its Californian stamps are at the top of the far slope opposite where you are standing, just this side of the mine's boundary with South Crofty and Old Cook's Kitchen and to the left of the part-buried chimney stack. The portal of the unfinished decline (spiral) shaft of South Crofty Mine is lower down the slope **(3)**. Some ruined buildings formerly visible in this area are said to have included the old Dolcoath mine smithy where it is believed parts of Richard Trevithick's 1801 steam locomotive were made. The main London-Penzance railway line runs on an embankment across the valley to the right, hiding from view Brea village.

Proceeding south now along the track, you start by passing through an area which used to be covered by mine ponds. *As the track curves right, take the narrower path# going left, crossing the footbridge over the railway* **(4)** *after about 50 yards.* Looking left as you pass over the railway

---

(2) The ore from South Crofty, apart from a few small parcels still treated on site, is now transported to the mill at Wheal Jane, near Truro, for processing.

(3) This shaft was begun prior to the 1985 tin price collapse. Though at a standstill at the time of writing, it is intended to enable self-propelled rock-handling machinery to reach the mine's deep active levels. Robinson's Shaft, which nowadays is used only for handling men and materials, could then be closed. In such an event, there is a long-term plan to convert the buildings and equipment at Robinson's Shaft into a major mining museum, which the area badly needs in order to encourage tourism.

(4) The present line follows the course of the Hayle Railway, built in order to link the port of Hayle with Camborne and Redruth, with later branches to Portreath, Roskear, Crofty and

bridge you can see in the far distance, beyond the engine house of South Tincroft, Carn Brea Mine's Old Stamps engine house and the mine's peculiar, stepped arsenic stack. The two preserved engine houses of East Pool are also visible from here, but to see Robinson's 80-inch pumping-engine house at South Crofty beyond the rusty building you have to walk a short distance along the field path. As you enter the field, notice the rusty bridge rails used as railway fence posts. These are relics of Brunel's broad gauge which lasted here until May 1892.

Continue ahead, passing through a small wooden gate before reaching a narrow country road. The area surrounding the track you have just come along is another one formerly used for ponds by Dolcoath - the remains of some of them were clearly recognisable until very recently (5)- and the last part of the track follows roughly the course of the main Dolcoath leat, which brought water to the mine, taking it from the Red River much higher up, near Bolenowe. The leat passed in front of the cottage on the other side of the road, where red "tin sand" (local waste used instead of clay) still marks the course of it, and part of the embankment, complete with revetment, has survived on the north side of the railway line, as will be mentioned again later.

2 *Turn right at the road,* which runs uphill and soon brings you to the large and unusual winding-engine house (6) at Williams' Shaft (7) of Dolcoath Mine. *Take the downhill path# on the right just this side of the engine-house and turn immediately left into a shallow depression.* You may have to fight your way to reach it. **Please note that it is dangerous to enter the building** except on the calmest of days: the west gable end wall

---

Tresavean mine near Lanner. It opened in 1837, mainly as a mineral line. In 1846 it was taken over by the West Cornwall Railway, and in 1889 by the GWR. In its early days this section was only single-track; the rails were where the left-hand track runs now.

(5) Kerrier District Council have recently carried out landscaping works on the old pond which was close to the surviving section of the main leat but just this side of the railway line. There are the remains of sluice gates. The pond and environs were very toxic, and dry, windy weather sometimes used to create toxic dust-storms. Covering so-called contaminated land with topsoil is a new threat to mine ruins in this part of Cornwall, and is opposed by conservation bodies. It is probably necessary here owing to the proximity of houses.

(6) The horizontal 2-cylinder winding engine, built by local firm Holman Brothers, could not be placed far enough back from the shaft without encroaching on the road. The unusual step was therefore taken of mounting it on rails so that it could travel sideways a maximum distance of 16 ft whilst hoisting. In this way the winding ropes maintained a straight approach to the "poppet heads" (pulley wheels over the shaft) with no tendency to jump off. The traversing arrangement was known as Morgans' patent, but no other examples are known to the writers. It is said that the joints in the swivel stand in the steam pipe to the engine to allow it to move were very hard to keep steam-tight. This stand was housed in an annexe still traceable at the east end of the house. The exhaust pipe was not similarly articulated but simply moved along with the engine.

(7) This vertical shaft was sunk between 1895 and 1912 to meet the Dolcoath main lode (which dips south) in depth - hence its position well south of the older workings. It is 17 ft 6 in in diameter and is the deepest in Cornwall, 3,000 ft below the collar. At the bottom of the shaft was an underground chamber containing a battery of electric pumps. In 1912 this was a major technical advance in Cornwall. The shaft area is now fenced off for safety.

Preparations being made for
the first sod ceremony before
work started on sinking
Williams' Shaft.
(The ceremony took place
on 26th October 1895.)

The interior of the winding-
engine house at Williams'
Shaft, October 1993.

collapsed in the winter of 1991-2, for example, leaving an arch over the door, which itself collapsed the following year. It is hoped that the building, which is to become a scheduled monument, will be stabilised by the Mineral Tramways Project as part of the Kerrier District Council's Derelict Land Programme in 1994-5. Along the two long wall faces inside can be seen the remains of cast-iron brackets which used to support toothed racks along which the engine crawled, and a rear walkway to provide access to the engine. The large opening in the right (north-west) wall is where the winding ropes from the drum passed to the shaft headframe outside. The depression in the ground at the nearest (north-east) end of the engine house is where the steam pipe swivel stand stood

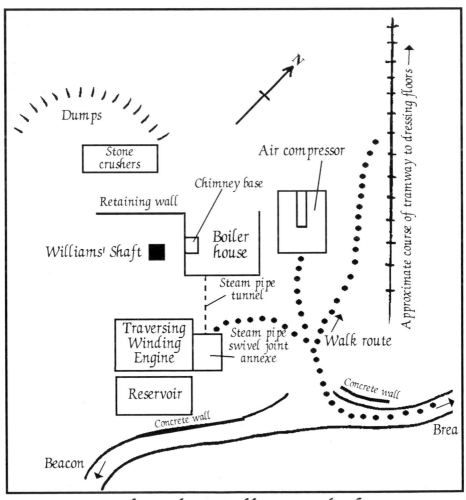

Dolcoath - Williams' Shaft

The traversing winding engine at Williams' Shaft, from Holman's literature (above), and derelict after the mine closed.

which allowed the engine to move. A part-circle of boiler plating visible in the ground appears to be the base of the main swivel since it lines up exactly with a small, square, shallow tunnel leading northwards which housed the steam main from the boiler house. A concrete tank behind the engine house probably contained boiler-feed and cooling water, while the exhaust pipe, which moved with the engine, went out through an opening low down in the south-west gable end.

The path runs downhill, and almost immediately you pass, on your left, the massive concrete foundations of the air-compressor machinery **(8)** which supplied underground rockdrills.

If you climb on to these foundations you will, in clear weather, be rewarded with the panoramic view mentioned in the introductory note. Among the mining features visible from here is the one surviving engine-house ruin of the Stray Park section of Dolcoath, which you can visit later on this walkabout; it is well to the left, and not easily noticed because of the trees that almost hide it from this angle. Much closer and very prominent is Dolcoath's Harriett's Shaft engine house, with the miners' dry behind and the electricians' store to the right, beside the road and railway. In the centre of the view, just beyond the railway line, look for two short sections of revetted embankment. The one on the left carried the tramway which took the ore from a now obscured shaft down the hill from Williams' to the stamps at the old mine; the other carried the main Dolcoath leat, mentioned earlier. Further right and quite distant you can glimpse the tower of Tuckingmill Church; close to that, on its left, is New Roskear Shaft, which today South Crofty uses for ventilation to combat radon gas. The square stack there appears identical to the one which formerly stood between us and the shaft and may have been built to the same drawing. Since the air compressor and Williams' electric pumping equipment were moved to New Roskear after Dolcoath's closure in 1921, this may be no coincidence ....! The large black building near that was Holman's Roskear Boiler Works, the terminus of the Roskear branch line mentioned earlier, which left the main line just west of the Stray Park engine house and remained in use until 1963. Looking still further right, a mass of old mine buildings can be seen, as mentioned at the earlier viewpoint. To the left of the foundations you are standing on, at a lower level, is a small ruined building which contained the engine's surface condenser, while further to the left a larger low-level area housed the boilers. The square stone base of the stack survives on the far side of the boiler house. Inside the fenced-off shaft area beyond can be seen a rusty gantry. This was erected over the shaft during World War 2 when it provided an emergency water supply. Downslope from the shaft is the foundation of a battery of stone crushers

---

(8) The air compressor which stood on the twin foundation blocks was a cross-compound 2-stage machine built in Lancashire, believed by Walker Bros. of Wigan. The boilers for both engines occupied the depressed area filled with bushes to the north-west of the winding house. A substantial square masonry base on the south-west side of the depression is the base of the former square chimney stack, the rest having been of brick. After Dolcoath's closure the compressor was moved to New Roskear Shaft, near Tuckingmill, where its house still stands.

and the waste tip. To the right of the air compressor foundation beside the path one of the mountings of a cylindrical air receiver lurks among the bushes.

Continue downhill, past some cottages, across a wider track, and through a gateway (no gate). In front of you and to the right of the path is the site of one of the large ponds which once served the mine. (See footnote 5.) The route of the tramway incline linking Williams' Shaft with the rest of the mine approximately followed this path.

3 *Turn sharp left, following a Public Footpath sign, and then right where a tarmacked path crosses. This brings you to a modern housing estate. Turn right (Tremayne Park), then left (Trecarrack Road). When you reach the main road (Lower Pengegon), cross the railway line on your right to Harriett's Shaft.* The first building encountered there, on the left beside the road, is the prominent former electricians' shop, now a club. It is said that this building doubled as a morgue when fatal accidents occurred at the mine. Right beside it is the site of the railway's Dolcoath Halt, a timber structure opened at the turn of the century in the expectation of a greatly increased workforce at the mine which never actually materialised. On the opposite (east) side of the road beyond the footbridge is Dolcoath Siding, by which rail-borne supplies reached the mine. It was used in more recent times for filling milk tanks bound for London, before this precious commodity began going by road.

Close to the electricians' shop is the engine house of Harriett's pumping engine **(9)**. The shaft is on the opposite (north) side, and the ruined walls on the west side belonged to the boiler house. The shaft was open at the time of writing, and none-too-securely fenced off; **until it is securely capped you should on no account venture inside the fencing.** The engine house is beginning to collapse into the shaft; it is due to be underpinned and a new reinforced shaft collar built under the shaft-capping programme.

The ground between the shaft and the miners' "dry", now in use by Cornwall College, was taken away in recent times and treated to give a tin recovery, leaving a deep depression. The dry itself was built in 1888, and was heated by steam pipes from the pumping engine's boiler house. Note the black blocks used in the walls as an architectural feature. These consist of "scoria", the solidified slag from copper smelting. (Near the end of section 5 is a hint as to the likely source of this.) Huge quantities of scoria like this were produced by the smelter at Copperhouse, Hayle, and scoria blocks were used in abundance for building there. (See "A View from Trencrom", Walk 7, for further details.)

---

(9) The engine had a 60-inch cylinder when supplied by the Perran Foundry in 1860 but in 1885 it was re-cylindered to 65 inches. This engine continued at work till the end of the mine, by which time it was pumping from a depth of 470 fathoms (measured not vertically but on the underlie) below adit. The stack has lost its upper brickwork. While the shaft is still open, note the mountings for the balance bob on the east side of the collar. On the west side, a shallow tunnel leading off the shaft is probably part of the circulation system for the engine's condenser, the cooling pond being in this direction.

Harriett's Shaft, Dolcoath -
the pumping engine at work,
with the smithy on the right;
and the engine house
as it was in October 1993

Close to the north-west corner of the building is a patch infested by the knotweed which is such a menace in these parts. Somewhere amongst that, or just beyond, is the Dolcoath Man-Engine Shaft (10), which may have been linked to the dry by an inclined tunnel or underground stairway, like the one at Levant.

A short extension to the walk to include Stray Park mine, absorbed into Dolcoath in the mid-19th century, is recommended. *Head west from the miners' dry to a perimeter path which runs to the left when you reach the high wire fence. Follow this round to the right, parallel to the railway,* glimpsing the big engine house of Condurrow United mine up on the ridge to the south (left). *The path emerges on to a track which brings one to a tarmac road (Foundry Road)* (11). *Turn left over the railway, using the road bridge or the new footbridge, officially opened in March 1994. The bridge was brought here from its previous site in Penryn.* The road bridge bears the date 1896 - the year when the track was doubled. *Now turn right into Park Lane.* The bungalow on the right is built on the site of the ore bin of Stray Park mine (12), and may even stand on the same foundations. The ore bin marked the western extremity of the mine tramway. Just beyond is the engine house, on private land, and inaccessible when we last visited because of a jungle of 8-foot-high knotweed. On the opposite side of the road is the site of a mine pond and a rope walk, now a private garden. (13)

4 *Return to Harriett's Shaft by the same route.* The garage opposite the end of Park Lane stands on the site of another rope walk, fragments of one

(10) The man-engine was the main means of reaching the mine's deeper levels from its year of installation (1854) until it was replaced by man-riding skips in Harriett's Shaft in 1897. By then Man-Engine Shaft had reached the 248 fathom level. The rotative beam engine which drove the man-engine stood 54 yd to the west, its site now being lost under Holman Compair's fenced-off testing area. To work the skips in Harriett's Shaft a 2-cylinder horizontal engine built by Worsley Mesnes (pronounced "Main") of Wigan was erected on the east side of the dry. Its foundations are now mostly buried under a dump of small stone. After Dolcoath's closure this engine was moved to New Roskear Shaft, mentioned earlier. In the 1970s, being still intact, it was the subject of a preservation venture in Lancashire which sadly failed.

(11) Foundry Road is so named because its lower (north) end ran right through the works of Holman Bros, by whom several Dolcoath engines were built or rebuilt. The site is now largely occupied by a Tesco superstore.

(12) Stray Park is another old mine which finally became part of Dolcoath in 1870. There were earlier pumping engines here but the one which concerns us was a 60-inch purchased from Pentireglaze Mine, beyond Padstow, in 1864. It was re-cylindered to 64 inches and then in 1900 was entirely rebuilt by Holman Bros with a 65-inch cylinder. Even the house was rebuilt, but the old engine beam and chimney stack were retained. If it can be seen under the ivy, the stack has in recent times almost completely fallen away from the house which, being much newer, is still in fair condition. The shaft, still open, is on the side nearest the railway, while the site of the winding engine to the west has disappeared under bungalows. It has been said that nothing good was ever found in Stray Park. This no doubt explains why Dolcoath tried to sell the mine off again in 1888, but without success.

(13) In the days of hemp ropes for hoisting the wear rate on them was alarming: at a busy shaft they could require replacement every few weeks. To counter this large mines like Dolcoath produced their own in long sheds known as rope walks.

wall of which could be seen until recent times running parallel to the railway at the top of the cutting. Look left as you cross the railway to see one of the Stray Park shafts, surrounded by a fence, on the side of the cutting near the engine house. Where the railway curves round out of sight is where an express train travelling westwards was derailed by a snowdrift in the region's "Great Blizzard" of 1891. The track you turn right on to immediately after crossing the railway begins by following the route of the westernmost end of the tramway linking Stray Park with Dolcoath. The 22-inch-gauge tramway crossed what is now the road bridge (perhaps the rails and granite setts are still there, under the tarmac). For many years after the rails were taken up the tramway route eastwards was used as a footpath, and there was an outcry when Holmans erected their tall fence across it. As you continue along the narrow path which runs beside the railway, notice the old iron aqueduct or launder crossing the line, which once brought more water to the mine. *Go on past the Harriett's Shaft engine house to the road (Lower Pengegon).*

5 *There, cross and turn left.* After a few yards you will pass a small, dilapidated brick building on the left side of the road; this was a weighbridge house, possibly but not certainly connected with the mine. *When you reach a turning on the left (Dolcoath Avenue)* **(14)**, *take the wide track or dirt road on the right,* which follows roughly the course of the Dolcoath tramway mentioned in point 4. It ran on an embankment and crossed Lower Pengegon road on a bridge, all sign of which has vanished. The now featureless ground on the left of the track was the location of some of the earliest engines at Dolcoath, at Old Sump Shaft; recent shaft capping has buried what little evidence of mine buildings survived here, but the scavenging of burrows for ore recovery exposed other ruins in the vicinity which can still be seen. **(15)** In the same area, recent excavation has exposed a massive bank of cinder and slag which is possibly the site of one of the earliest copper smelting works to be built in Cornwall. (Some details of this are given by W.H.Pascoe in *The History of the Cornish Copper Company,* Truran 1981.) This area simply cries out for scientific examination. The well preserved tall building on the high ground north of the cinder bank housed an air compressor **(16)**.

6 *Soon you reach the point where the track turns right towards Williams'*

---

(14) Like Dolcoath Halt, many of the houses in Dolcoath Avenue were built by the mine in its last days for an anticipated influx of miners. The walls are made of concrete: "lovely and warm in winter but very hard to drive a nail in," as one resident put it.
(15) One survival is the base of Old Sump beam whim, which stood some distance to the south of the shaft, on the other side of the broad track. Further east, to the left of the track leading to Williams' Shaft, is the exposed base of a furnace of some kind, possibly a reverberatory calciner, while nearer at hand is a substantial block of coarse masonry, the base of a steam capstan serving New Sump Shaft. (Note the use of old firebars to form the bolt tunnels.)
(16) An inverted vertical "Champion" type air compressor was installed here in 1883. It consisted of two machines which could either run coupled for maximum output or be separated for maintenance, and the air pipes were led down New Sump Shaft to supply underground drills, which were coming into vogue at the time to supersede hand drilling.

Shaft, crossing a bridge over the railway. A few yards away in that direction is the base of the Old Sump Whim engine house. *Don't go that way, but continue ahead for a few yards.* When we last visited this spot, proceeding in that direction entailed scrambling over a low earth-and-rubble embankment which had very recently been put there in order to discourage travellers and fly-tippers. (Those who took the short cut at point 3 have to turn right, of course, to cross this embankment.) The low and almost unidentifiable ruins of several early mine buildings lie scattered in the area you have now reached. The two nearest are described in footnote (13).

Climb the narrow path# (though it scarcely deserves to be called a path) on the left, which heads roughly towards the compressor house. This quickly brings you to the most historically interesting surface remains at Dolcoath, around New Sump Shaft (17). The bed of the last engine to work here with its six projecting cylinder hold-down bolts can now be seen after lying buried for many years. New Sump was the deepest on the mine before Williams' Shaft was sunk, and served the 550-fm level. (This is not the true depth as levels at Dolcoath were measured on the underlie, or

---

(17) About 1775 the adventurers erected a 45-inch-cylinder engine here, obtained secondhand from Calloose Mine, near Leedstown, and modified by Richard Trevithick in about 1799. It had the beam underneath. In 1781 Watt's "Great Engine" was erected to pump from the same shaft. It had a 63-inch cylinder, was double acting, and was arranged like the later Bull engines with the cylinder directly over the shaft. It is difficult today to visualise how the shaft head looked with these two engines at work.

The sunken, level area with the six great bolts projecting from the floor is the site of the third and most famous engine to pump from this shaft - it replaced the two older engines after being set to work in August 1816. This was the first true Cornish beam engine, designed by Richard Trevithick but with its erection entrusted to two of his assistants, Jeffree and Gibble, following their chief's sudden departure for Peru. It had a 76-inch cylinder supplied by Neath Abbey works in South Wales, a beam cast at the Perran Foundry and other parts made in the mine's own workshops. Save for brief interruptions this venerable machine worked day and night until 1912 when its duties were taken over by the electric pumps in Williams' Shaft. However in 1869 it had a major overhaul when the original cylinder was replaced by one of 85 inches to gain more power. It is this cylinder 9 which accounts for the present six holding-down bolts.

The engine house was very cramped, as can be seen by the present outline of the walls. The bob wall, too, was narrow for an engine of such size, judging by the surviving red brickwork: the gap in the middle of this marks the site of the "plug doorway" through which the driver could observe the working of the condenser air-pump and feed pump outside. When the bigger cylinder was fitted there was no longer any room for the staircase, so a five-sided wooden stairwell extension was built on the rear (west) wall of the house. It was very prominent in old photographs, and its outline now is just discernible. At the same time the house was heightened to accommodate kingpost and bridle reinforcement of the beam.

The present fascinating ruins at the head of the shaft lay buried until a few years ago when a limited archaeological dig was carried out by members of the Trevithick Society, led by Clive Carter. It is hoped that one day it will be resumed. The boiler house area on the north side of the engine house, where Trevithick installed his new Cornish boiler in 1811, is a particular focal point of interest.

The purpose of the relatively modern dwarf walls of yellow brick on the eastern edge of the shaft is not entirely clear; they probably supported the legs of a steel headgear erected over the shaft in connection with a new winding engine, described in the main walk details. The whole area around the shaft is, fortunately, protected and cannot be built on.

Old Sump Shaft, Dolcoath, on the left, and whim (right). Further away,
left of centre, is the very distinctive New Sump engine house.
The man to the left is standing on the tramway embankment.

New Sump engine house from the west showing the wooden
rear extension for the staircase added in 1869.
Tramway extension to stone crushers on right.

inclination, of the shaft.) It has recently been capped deep down and backfilled; now it is merely a depression in the ground beside the dwarf walls of yellow brick. Like most old shafts, much of it is on an underlie (that is, inclined at a shallow angle), only the top 180 fathoms being vertical. It underlies towards the south, the lowest levels in the mine being directly below Williams' Shaft, which was sunk vertically to meet them. North east of the shaft can be seen three prominent concrete mounting blocks. The tallest (right-hand or southern one) carried a stone crusher erected early this century. The other two, half-hidden by ivy, carried a horizontal winding engine purchased secondhand from the Wheal Cock section of Botallack mine in 1893-4. (See Walk 6.) This engine was so aligned that it could hoist from either New Sump or New East shaft, being situated roughly midway between them. New steel headgears were erected over the two shafts at the same time. The area surrounding these remains is due to be scheduled and fenced off for archaeological interpretation.

Leaving New Sump Shaft and heading north, as you approach the compressor house you pass on your left the area where the mine's stables are thought to have been. This part of the mine was littered with unsightly rubbish when we were there - hardly an encouragement to prospective tenants for the compressor house, which was being offered to let by the Cornwall County Council. The CCC has made a good job of reroofing the compressor house, using scantle slate. *Walk through the gap between the compressor house and the two shed-like buildings.* Temporary and comparatively flimsy though the latter look, they have been there for at least half a century: Kenneth remembers them as kitchens preparing school meals during World War 2. At that time the compressor house was being used as a canteen serving the former Dolcoath Technical College, whose premises consisted of the buildings behind the railings on the other side of the road. The large house set back was built as Dolcoath's count house, replacing the one destroyed by fire in 1895. The Technical College has since been re-formed as the Cornwall College in a new building at Pool.

Turn right to return to the parking place. Notice as you walk the remains of a few half-buried wooden sleepers, showing the course of the mine's tramway, leading to the aforementioned hump in the road, the site of a level crossing.

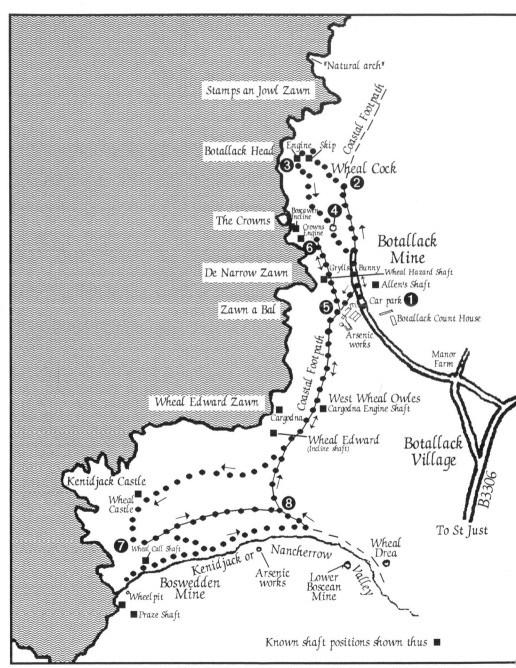

"Natural arch"

Stamps an Jowl Zawn

Coastal Footpath

Botallack Head — Engine   Skip
❸   Wheal Cock
                                   ❷

Boscawen
Incline   ❹

The Crowns —   Crowns
                     Engine
                                   Botallack
❻   Mine

De Narrow Zawn   Grylls   Bunny   Wheal Hazard Shaft
                                       Allen's Shaft
                     ❺   Car park ❶
Zawn a Bal   Botallack Count House

                     Arsenic
                     works
                                       Manor
                                       Farm
Wheal Edward Zawn
                     West Wheal Owles
                     Cargodna Engine Shaft
         Cargodna   Botallack
                     Wheal Edward   Village
                     (Incline shaft)

Kenidjack Castle
   Wheal   B3306
   Castle
                     ❽
                                       To St Just
❼ Wheal Call Shaft
                                   Wheal
           Kenidjack or Nancherrow Drea
             Arsenic   Valley
   Wheelpit Boswedden works Lower
             Mine   Boscean
   Praze Shaft   Mine

Known shaft positions shown thus ■

Botallack and Neighbouring Mines

6
BOTALLACK MINE, WHEAL OWLES & WHEAL CASTLE
with optional detours to
WHEAL COCK & BOSWEDDEN MINE

Regarded purely as a walk in dramatic and beautiful scenery, this is the clear winner among the six covered in *Exploring Cornish Mines,* and in terms of the mining remains it must be a contender with Basset Mines for top place. The basic walk described is under three miles in length and not very strenuous, any uphill walking being on quite gentle gradients. Two extensions are suggested. The first, to Wheal Cock, adds nearly a mile to the route; it involves a little scrambling on rough slopes and a few hundred yards of walking along a narrow path close to the cliff edge, which would be nerve-racking for some, and possibly dangerous in windy weather. That could, however, be avoided by retracing your steps along the coast path, further inland. The second extension, down to Boswedden Mine in the Kenidjack Valley, is short but requires a fairly stiff climb back to the level of the main route. There are no pubs, cafés, shops or public toilets along the way, but the Queen's Arms in Botallack village is not far inland from the parking place.

LOCATION (Botallack): A little over a mile north of St Just-in-Penwith. Grid reference: SW 364 332.

HOW TO GET THERE   **By car:** Take the coast road (B3306) north from St Just. After nearly a mile, at Botallack village, fork left, passing the Queen's Arms. Ignore the first minor turning on the left, but take the second, at Manor Farm. This narrow road heads towards the cliffs and soon deteriorates to a rough track. After about a quarter of a mile you will pass on the right a row of holiday cottages built on the site of Botallack mine's sawmill, then the mine's weighbridge house and, set back from the road, the carpenter's shop and the rather grand former count house of the mine; there is quite a large area for parking on the right just beyond that. The long wall beside the car park was part of a headquarters complex comprising stores, smithy, etc., and included a shed for the traction engine used for road-hauling the ore to Penzance when the mine last worked.

By public transport: There are fairly frequent bus services using the coast road north and east from St Just. Please consult current timetables. Any of these services would take you to Botallack village, from which there is a walk of about half a mile to the cliffs at Botallack mine.

WALK DIRECTIONS AND DESCRIPTION OF MINING FEATURES

A visit to the site of Wheal Cock (about three-quarters of a mile to the north), which worked for the later part of its history as part of Botallack, is strongly recommended, both for its historical interest and also for the

BOTALLACK MINE

"The Botallack mine is probably the most remarkable in the world .... a wonder, showing the enterprise of man, and his marvellous control over the earth on which he moves." (Thomas Spargo, 1865) The Botallack area, where the mineral lodes were exceptionally prominent in the cliffs, was among the earliest to be mined in the St Just district. A large number of small independent enterprises combined under the name of Botallack - many of them by the end of the 18th century, some others not until the start of the 20th. Wheal Cock had already driven levels under the sea by 1778, when William Pryce wrote about the "thundering roar" of the Atlantic waves and the moving rocks on the sea bed heard by the miners below. The foresight and determination of one man, Steven Harvey James, kept Botallack alive during hard times in the late 1830s, when prices were low and most of the tin and copper from the shallower levels had already been recovered, and ushered in the period of its greatest prosperity. Its first royal visitor was Queen Victoria, in 1846. From the late '40s onwards it expanded steadily, taking over several neighbouring mines and venturing much further under the sea with the aid of the Boscawen Diagonal Shaft, begun in 1858. Its name was a tribute to the owner of the mineral rights, Lord Falmouth. The descent of the new shaft by the Prince and Princess of Wales in 1865 went ahead despite a horrific accident in April 1863, when the chain attached to the iron gig broke as eight men and a boy were being hauled to the surface. This led to the substitution of wire rope for the chain: eventually chains were totally superseded by wire ropes throughout Cornwall and elsewhere. After the '60s, despite the mine's fame as a "tourist attraction", its fortunes fluctuated, and problems caused by low prices or disappointing output were partly offset by sales of arsenic; but by the '90s so much cheap tin was being produced abroad that ruin was facing all Cornish mines, and when a cloudburst flooded the then richest part of Botallack, Wheal Cock, in November 1894, followed by more underground flooding in February 1895, the mine's shareholders had no choice but to pay off the workforce and sell the surface plant. Twelve years later came an ambitious attempt to reopen the mine, and most of the remains on the clifftop date from this period. Unfortunately, the lease granted to the new company by Lord Falmouth stipulated that a new shaft - known as Allen's, after Francis Allen, one of the directors - had to be sunk inland at the point where the modern headgear now stands. This was a bad mistake, because the best prospects for rich new discoveries of ore lay well out to sea. For three-quarters of a century from 1914 Botallack was abandoned to the elements. In 1980 - the year when Botallack received its third royal visitor, Queen Elizabeth II - Geevor Mine decided to extend its workings into Botallack, and efforts were made to refurbish Allen's Shaft, but the crash in tin prices of 1985 prevented any underground development from taking place.

spectacular scenery in which it is set. The following directions assume you will start your tour of Botallack with Wheal Cock, but if you prefer to leave it out, turn left where stated below.

1 *From the recommended parking place turn right (north),* passing the tall headframe at Allen's Shaft on your right. This and other nearby relics of the 20th century mining activity at Botallack are described later. *(Now, if you prefer to omit the exploration of Wheal Cock, take the downhill path sharp left - i.e. the coastal footpath, as indicated by an acorn sign, and read on from line 5 in point 4.)* As you continue north along the main track - which, incidentally, is the official coastal footpath - on your right, immediately beyond Allen's, is a shallow but quite extensive excavation, the result of openwork mining which is thought to date back several centuries. It is part of what is known as Grylls Bunny. The pit remains quite impressive despite the fact that material from Allen's Shaft was dumped in it between 1906 and 1914, and some gunnises have survived on the inland side, but perhaps the most interesting part of the Bunny is on the opposite side of the track, where several such gunnises can be seen if you are prepared to scramble around on the rough little paths below. There is a "warren" of small chambers and tunnels where the mineralised rock has been removed, and this is thought by some to be the reason for the name, but the Cornish word, "bonny", a bunch of ore, seems a more likely origin. "Bonny" may well be a corruption of "carbona".

Continue along the main track. Some distance away across the fields to the right can be seen the lone stack at Nineveh Shaft - one of very few tangible remains of the inland part of Botallack. A rotative pumping engine once stood there. On the seaward side, some 50 m away, is the ruinous base of the house that contained a small whim engine which hauled from Wheal Hazard Shaft, partway down the cliff. We shall see this later. As you approach a group of farm buildings, notice on your left the small stone bridge with its arched opening blocked. Opinions differ as to what ran beneath the bridge: a tramway is shown here on the 1880 OS map, but a leat feeding the cliffside stamps also followed a similar route. Whatever it was, its course can still be traced for some distance, despite the thick scrub.

2 Just past the farm buildings take the fairly wide path on the left which reaches the cliff edge a few yards to the right of a white triangulation station marker, and leads you straight to the massive concrete loadings on which the Wheal Cock horizontal whim engine **(1)** was mounted.

A short distance to the north are Wheal Cock's Skip Shaft and Engine (pumping) Shaft, both securely fitted with welded steel grills early in 1993. Engine Shaft is at a lower level, very near the cliff edge, and not visible from the site of the whim; it was from this shaft that the engine hauled. The dumps of waste here are very extensive and rich in mineral: the loose

---

(1) This was a twin-cylinder horizontal engine, believed built by Holman Bros of Camborne. It worked here from 1892 until the mine's closure in 1895 (or possibly only until the 1894 flood), and was then moved to Dolcoath New Sump Shaft.

rock which abounds on this site displays some attractive coloration and is regularly used by mining students for mineral identification studies. The "natural arch" down by the water at the northern side of Stamps an Jowl Zawn may in fact be at least partially man-made, since it almost certainly indicates where the mineralised lode once ran.

Continue by walking to Skip Shaft and then a few yards further along the track, to the point where there are ruined mine "service buildings" up on your right. We now suggest that you take the narrow path across the waste tips down to Engine Shaft. You will need to pick your way with care and do a little scrambling, because the original path has been cut away near the bottom of the slope.

Here and there can still be seen the remains of eye-bolts driven into the rocks; to these were attached guy ropes or cables designed to hold in place the very exposed, tall headframe at Skip Shaft. It is said that this structure used to sway alarmingly in strong winds. Its height was probably dictated by the use of a hoisting rope running along the clifftop from Carn whim, above the Crowns, a good half mile away. Better examples of the eye-bolts can be seen a little later.

The top part of the impressive (but possibly not very stable, so beware!) retaining wall on the seaward side of Engine Shaft probably includes a fragment of the building - already in ruins by 1880 - which housed a 24-inch pumping engine **(2)**. Part of its boiler house can still be seen, and, closer to the shaft, small concrete slabs on which stood electrical equipment in connection with the submersible pump used in the abortive 1908-14 working. Now that the grid is in place over the shaft you can safely peer into its depths, and the daylight entering through what appears to be a cave-in close to the adit means that you can see quite a long way down. This is probably the best view from surface of a disused mineshaft to be had in Cornwall. The circular stone collar is of relatively recent origin. In 1892 the shaft was enlarged for skip hoisting and for winding men, for which purpose the horizontal whim on the clifftop was erected. Lower down its shape changes to rectangular. Like most Cornish shafts it is not vertical and develops a seaward underlie to follow the lode. The shaft is ten times deeper than can be seen, 215 fathoms below the collar. **(3)**

---

(2) This engine was erected in 1842. That such a small engine could take the mine down to a depth of of 190 fm below adit (the adit is just above high-tide level) is due to the natural dryness of the coastal mines of this area. Most of the water entering Cornish mines is due to rainfall percolating through the upper strata; but for workings beneath the sea bed, the sea provides a natural protection - in other words, the sea keeps the water out!

(3) From available evidence it is not possible to be certain how hoisting at Wheal Cock was done at different periods. Originally it was from Skip Shaft and probably Engine Shaft too, the 16-inch beam whim mentioned in the next paragraph of the text probably having an upright axle drum. KB's theory is that in 1875 when Boscawen Shaft closed (see later details), this whim was abandoned and Crowns whim redeployed to haul from Skip Shaft, using the tall headgear. There would have been a long line of pulley stands to support the rope over a distance of some 350 yd. Photographs show only one poppet head for a single skip. J.H.Trounson used to say that Crowns whim was deployed at Wheal Cock for a period. The Holman winder of 1892 was associated with the enlargement of Engine Shaft, as mentioned by Cyril Noall (pp 135-6).

Looking up the Wheal Cock engine shaft to the grid recently placed over the circular collar. (Photograph by Adrian Katsikides)

Looking north across Stamps an Jowl Zawn to the "natural arch" in the cliffs. Note the eye-bolt at the bottom right-hand corner of this picture.

3 *Now head back south, using the narrow path.* It is well defined but quite steep in places, and, as we warned at the start, runs close to the cliff edge. Embedded in the rocks beside this path at the start are at least three rusty but fairly complete eye-bolts, as mentioned earlier. Almost immediately the path brings you close to the site of the earlier Wheal Cock beam whim engine house: you can scramble up by means of a small and rather overgrown path to the small level area where it stood. From there a ruined flue goes steeply up, showing that there was once a stack quite close to the place where the horizontal whim engine was later sited. The beam whim was quite small with only a 16-inch cylinder and used an upright axle winding drum, like others in the St Just district, so that it could haul from Skip Shaft, Engine Shaft and possibly others.

The cliff-edge path soon takes you to past Botallack Head and on to a comparatively level area covered with mine waste. From here, if you choose your vantage point carefully, you can look down to the remains of the whim engine house at Wheal Button: parts of the boiler house and stack can still be seen. The site of the shaft on a short promontory close to the sea is also visible. A short distance further south on the clifftop stood the Carn whim engine house. **(4)** Its truncated stack is still a landmark though nothing of the house remains. Still visible is the stone block which carried the footstep bearing of the upright axle of the winding drum. Go to the cliff edge a few yards from that to find the top of the steep skip road shown on the old photographs of the Boscawen incline shaft. In places a channel had to be cut in the cliff face to admit the skip road, and at the top fragments of stonework show where it terminated. A few of the eye-bolts driven into the rock to help hold the wooden skip-road structure in place can still be found, but precise details of this and other structures which once stood here are elusive. Elsewhere on this level area can be found traces of a pond and fine leavings from the stamps. Glimpses of the Crowns pumping-engine house and Pearce's whim house, which served the

---

(4) (This note is included here because it relates to the Crowns Whim, but to understand it fully you need some knowledge of parts of Botallack Mine visited later on this tour.) The hoisting arrangements at the Boscawen incline shaft (worked 1862 to 1875) are as follows. After Wheal Button engine and shaft had been used to sink Boscawen, the engine was almost certainly (though definite proof is lacking) moved to its new position where its house and boiler house survive. It was an all-enclosed beam whim very similar to the one preserved at Levant Mine. It hauled a single wagon, or gig, running on a rail track on the incline which was generally at a 32.5° angle to the horizontal. The engine stood some 70 yd from the shaft portal, the intervening space being occupied by a timber trestle carrying the rail track above a small rocky beach. The gig was used for men or rock. The men simply entrained from, or detrained on to, a footway carried on the trestle. The rock was discharged from the skip into an ore-pass (or ore bin) below the trestle. From here it was fed into a special skip running on a nearly vertical track set in a man-made cleft in the cliff. A solitary iron tie rod dangling down the cliff shows how the timberwork was anchored back against the fierce Atlantic gales. At the top the skip road levelled off to the horizontal, enabling the skip to be manoeuvred to a small set of tin stamps. The engine which drove these stamps also drove the skip: it was another all-enclosed beam whim with an upright axle drum. Known as Crowns Whim, it had earlier been used to haul from Wheal Hazard Shaft, and after Boscawen's closure it was utilised to haul from Wheal Cock Skip Shaft, as noted earlier.

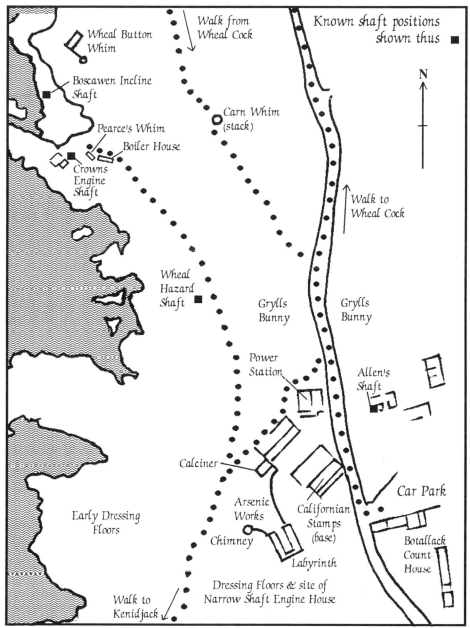

Botallack Mine: plan showing surface features

Boscawen Shaft, both much lower down the cliff, can also be gained from here, but viewpoints are risky, and the pumping-engine house is due to be visited later.

4 *Continue on the path ahead, which soon returns you to the coastal footpath close to the Bunny. Now take the downhill path (still the coastal footpath, as indicated by the acorn sign on the wooden post) which starts shortly before you reach the headframe at Allen's Shaft.*

On your left now are the remains of the early 20th century dressing floors and calciner (arsenic works) of Botallack, which we suggest you explore now before continuing the walk. The first, cinder-covered side path leads up to the remains of the power station, where little has survived apart from a battered arch in a cement-rendered stone wall. A rusty cable bracket projects from the seaward side of this wall. The building originally housed three electricity generators powered by gas engines. They supplied current to the submersible electric pumps used in this reworking, and also to the mill and calciner. The producer gas plant was at the rear; small coal from it can still be found in the cliff paths nearby. At a higher level on the south side of the power station stood the tin mill containing a battery of 40 heads of Californian stamps; the massive concrete base for this structure remains intact, along with the outlines of shaking tables, buddles and round frames, all ready for the tin which never materialised **(5)**. On the seaward side of that is the ruined arsenic calciner, with its power vault below, which has recently been converted into a "summer house". Outside stand the plinths for the calciner's electric drive. From the calciner to the nearby chimney runs the labyrinth or "lambreth" flue **(6)**.

Return to the coastal footpath.

5 *At the point where the path runs just below the tall chimney stack of the arsenic works, turn sharp right on to the much-used track or road leading gently down to the famous pair of engine houses at the Crowns.* Not far down the track there is the mouth of an exploratory adit at a slightly higher level on your right. At the time of writing this is still open and accessible, but entering it is <u>not</u> recommended under any circumstances. The remnant of a building on the right a little further down is thought to have been the original Botallack (or Crowns or Hazard?) count house.

---

(5) The main use of this plant was to process the old burrows for tin. Though the percentage recovery was low, the amount produced by this means was comparable with the disappointing results underground. Dines records an output of 100-150 tons of tin oxide a year during the last working, compared with some 14,500 tons during the preceding 100 years using more primitive equipment.

(6) In plan view the flue system describes a large U, finishing at the exceptionally tall, black-topped arsenic stack. There are two groups of condensing chambers, one each side of the U, and at the apex the flue crosses the site of the mine tramway by means of a bridge. The stack itself is older than the rest of the masonry work; the Abandoned Mine Plans suggest it served Botallack's steam stamps engine, to the boiler house of which it was linked by a short horizontal flue. This engine stood a little to the south and was a twin beam engine, also working pumps in Narrow Shaft. Only faint traces of this engine house survive, among the grass-grown burrows east of the coastal track. In the same area, half-hidden among the scrub can be discerned the remains of buddles and other features of 19th century dressing floors, together with traces of the arsenic works built by Botallack in 1875.

The Crowns engine houses about 1980, before the Carn Brea Mining Society began work on them; and work in progress about four years later.

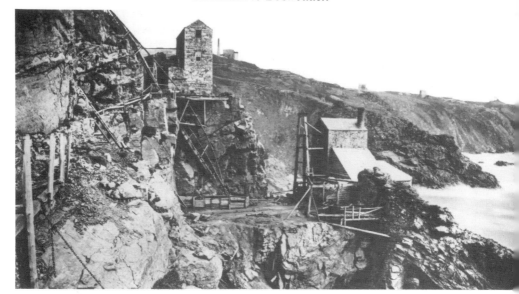

The Crowns section of Botallack after the Boscawen Incline Shaft had been abandoned. The closest engine house on the clifftop, with two bobs, was at Narrow Shaft; further right are Cargodna and Wheal Edward. The pumping engine nearest camera was still at work when this picture was taken.

Botallack: Pearce's whim as seen from the mouth of the Boscawen Shaft. (Photograph by Adrian Katsikides)

Just below that, on the seaward side of the track, is Wheal Hazard Shaft, though you need a practised eye to spot it, since it was recently capped. Take care not to trip over the stumps of fence posts which lurk in the grass beside the path. A wooden fence was demanded for safety reasons while conservation work was in progress on the Crowns engine houses in the 1980s but for environmental reasons it was removed afterwards. The stumps now give Wheal Hazard a new meaning! **(7)**

Of the two engine houses you are now approaching, the upper one is Pearce's whim which hauled from the incline shaft in 1862-75; the lower one is of the Crowns 36-inch pumping engine which drained this part of the mine from 1835 to 1895.

Just before the path steepens on its descent to the whim can be seen the area where the mortar was mixed and the operatives practised stone-laying as part of the conservation work mentioned above. Another former mine building used to stand here.

Now as you descend the steep track a splendid walled viewing area appears on the left. This is, in fact, what remains of the boiler house of Pearce's whim engine house adjacent. The twin flue exits at one end unite into one flue which turns left and can be traced running beneath the path and up the cliff to the circular base of the stack, which was never very tall **(8)**.

Pearce's whim-engine house has several interesting features **(9)**. The few steps beside it lead down to a promontory, accessible if you don't suffer from vertigo, from which the portal of Boscawen incline shaft can be seen in the distant rock face, half hidden by a fallen boulder. Now try to imagine the flimsy timber trestle structure descending at 32.5° from where you are standing, with the rail track plunging into the dark abyss, when a Force 12 was blowing from the south-west! Partway along the trestle was a wooden gateway: photographs show this to have been decorated with flowers and greenery on the occasion of the royal party's descent in 1865.

On your right, the smooth cleft in the cliff marks the site of the skip road up which ore was conveyed to the stamps attached to Carn whim. Note

---

(7) Its old meaning is presumably the same as that of Wheal Chance, quite a common name for Cornish mines. The physical dangers of sinking shafts in such locations as this are only too obvious, but the "hazard" referred to is more likely to relate to the fact that all such mining ventures were a risky business from the financial point of view.

(8) The practice of using an inclined flue in the cliff to reduce the cost of the stack was common in this area: it was also done with the beam whims at Wheal Cock and Wheal Button.

(9) The square cylinder bedstone survives at the east end of the house - a sure sign that the engine itself, which had a cylinder of about 24 inches, was scrapped after ceasing to work and not moved to another site. The square opening for the steam-pipe entry in the east wall of the house is on the seaward side, remote from the boiler house, reminding us that the engine came here secondhand from Wheal Button. (It was actually used there to sink Boscawen Shaft between 1858 and 1862, the two shafts meeting one another at shallow depth.) Inside the house the condenser pit and flywheel slot can be seen, as can a wall plaque commemorating the conservation work done in 1984-5 by the Carn Brea Mining Society. (The CBMS raised the funds for the project and was wholly responsible for its organisation and management.) Outside the house the massive block of masonry beside the steps recently formed in the path accommodated reduction gearing to the winding drum, which occupied a pit where the steps now are.

the hanging iron tie rod, if it is still there.

The path around the edge of the cliff to Wheal Button has been partly washed away in recent years and should not be attempted. Wheal Button Shaft, 185 fm deep below adit, can be seen distantly on a small promontory directly above Boscawen Shaft: the engine site, on a ledge above, cannot be seen from this point.

The rock in this area is a hard greenstone which made driving Boscawen Shaft very difficult. This led to the early decision to use a single skip in the shaft instead of two. The ultimate depth reached was 250 fm below sea level, where a small area was worked half a mile offshore prior to abandonment.

The block of masonry beside the whim is worth a second look - it has clearly been extended outwards at some time in its working life. This is almost certainly a reminder of the disaster in 1863: see the note on the history of Botallack. Changeover to wire rope would have meant having a narrower winding drum and hence realignment of the stonework each side of the drum pit.

The pumping-engine house is of equal interest owing to its great age, but scrambling down to it is not only dangerous but unnecessary. The engine was built by Harvey & Co and worked at a gentle pace for 60 years. Crowns Engine Shaft in front has been filled but was still open at the time of the 1907-14 fiasco as the base of electrical equipment bears witness. It is 135 fm deep. Prior to 1835 an even earlier engine pumped from it. Old engravings show its house to have stood on the grassy level area west of the shaft, at right angles to the later engine. The boiler house to the right of the engine house, which contained two Cornish boilers of dissimilar size, was unfortunately not included in the 1984 restoration for reasons of cost, and is slowly succumbing to the effects of weather and vandalism. When one discovers that the two engine houses are just perched on the rock with little in the way of foundations, one realises the daring of engineers and artisans of the last century in mounting machinery in such positions, and moreover getting it to work satisfactorily for many years!

When you return to the whim boiler-house area, it's worth pausing to look at the view again. The bare rock on which the Crowns pumping-engine house stood is best appreciated from here. The small, square opening in it is probably where the water pumped was discharged. Landmarks on the skyline to the left (south) include (left to right) Botallack's arsenic calciner and its impressive stack, Cargodna pumping-engine house and Wheal Edward stamps-engine house.

6 *Return the same way to rejoin the coastal footpath to Botallack's neighbour, Wheal Owles.*

Just below the arsenic works stack, a bed of tin sand in the path denotes the site of the mine's main 19th-century dressing floors. The present path runs right through them. The site of Botallack stamps engine which also pumped from Narrow Shaft can just be discerned, south of the calciner and left of the path.

Continue southwards on the coast path.

WHEAL OWLES

Like most if not all the other mines hereabouts, Wheal Owles (pronounced "Oals" or "Olds") consisted of a combination of many small old mines; for example, one called "Whele an Houl" was at work by 1725. (The name could mean "the sun mine", though "Owles" may derive from Cornish *als,* meaning cliff or shore: compare Penhalls Mine, described elsewhere in this book.) Wheals Edward, Drea, Grouse and Cargodna are perhaps the best known of them. The period of Wheal Owles' greatest prosperity was the 1860s, when it had 11 engines and "the staggering total of 29 miles of levels, 3 miles of adits, and an additional mile of levels being driven each year" (Cornwall Archaeological Unit: St Just Survey). Poor prices for metallic ores during the '70s and '80s led to the closure of most of the inland sections of the mine; the best prospects seemed to be under the sea. In 1884 the decision was taken to focus all efforts on the Cargodna section, known by this time as West Wheal Owles, and the clifftop pumping engine there was the only one that continued working. It was just before 9am on 10th January 1893 that miners at the 65-fathom level (below adit) in Cargodna broke through into the flooded 148-fathom level (measured from surface) of Wheal Drea - which according to the plans they were relying on was nearly 40 yd away from where they were working. The torrent of water that surged through the new levels with a roar described by one of the survivors as "louder than ten thousand thunders" was so devastating that, according to the St Just Survey, it created enough air pressure to blow out a big crater near the Kenidjack almshouses, a short way up the valley. (Cyril Noall, however, mentions the belief that the hole resulted from the sudden outflow of water, "the unsupported ground then collapsing to adit level.") Some of the mine waste that still forms a large heap below the Wheal Drea engine house was later used to fill it. Nineteen men and a boy were drowned - their bodies have never been recovered - and the management soon gave up any attempt to drain the mine. Nearly ten pages of Noall's book are devoted to the Wheal Owles disaster; he gives a particularly vivid account of the bravery and practical intelligence of James "Farmer" Hall, who saved the lives of at least five men; and he includes many other memorable details, such as the sad paragraph about the young miner called Thomas who was due to be married that day. The wedding was postponed at the Vicar's request, and Thomas was among those who died. One miner, Thomas Lutey, had had forebodings of tragedy, and for several days beforehand had taken to running through the workings shouting "Water! Water!" In the event, Thomas and his brother Richard narrowly escaped with their lives, but Thomas never went underground again. He earned a meagre living selling oranges in and around St Just, "walking along the roads with a shuffling gait, his eyes always fixed on the ground, as if he were expecting the earth to open under his feet."

The first ruined engine house you come to is the 36-inch pumping-engine house of Cargodna or West Wheal Owles. The engine shaft is rubbish-filled but the balance bob pit is clearly visible, leading off at an angle towards the path. Not far beyond that, a few scraps of walling and some foundations above the path to the left mark the site of the same mine's whim engine house. This clifftop part of Wheal Owles was not developed until about 1870.

Cargodna hoisting shaft is some way down the cliff to your right, and the whim, with a 24-inch cylinder, was purchased secondhand late in the mine's career, in 1882, to haul twin skips in this shaft. The skip road ran up the cliff from the shaft collar and terminated on the mound of waste on the seaward side of the path. A short detour to examine the remains of the whim-engine house reveals the footstep mounting for an upright-axle winding-drum above the path, with traces of grease and similar to the one seen earlier at the Crowns whim.

The third engine house, a little further on to the seaward, dates from about 1870 and housed a 28-inch multi-function rotative beam engine **(10)**. Unusually, the chimney stack was inside the rear corner of the house, but recent collapse of the wing wall on the landward side has destroyed much of it. **Owing to its ruinous state, this engine house is considered extremely dangerous to approach or enter. ("Quite lethal" is Clive Carter's phrase for it.)(11)**

It is impossible to give precise directions for a scramble down the cliff to find Cargodna Shaft, but if you do succeed you will find it protected by a square stone wall. It is 140 fm deep. A plaque was fixed to it by the Carn Brea Mining Society in 1993 commemorating the twenty miners who went down the shaft on 10 January 1893 and never returned. Further details about this disaster are included in the note on Wheal Owles.

A short way south is a site that for several years has been occupied by a group of travellers. Use the main track that runs on the inland side of that, and then take the grassy path which bears right - still the coastal footpath. After a few yards there is a gateway with a rough stile on the right side.

From this point you can see on the right the burrow at Wheal Edward

---

(10) There is evidence suggesting that at one time the engine had a "back bob" or auxiliary beam drawing water from a shaft at the rear. It is known from photographs that the engine originally drove an upright-axle winding-drum on the edge of the cliff to hoist from Cargodna Shaft downslope from the house, Wheal Edward incline shaft about 150m to the south-west, and possibly others. It also drove 16 heads of stamps aligned with the landward end of the crankshaft. Later the hoisting drum was dispensed with - it was probably moved to the 1882 whim - and the number of stamp heads doubled. The crankshaft mounting with the single flywheel slot is readily visible. Evidence of its ore-treatment function is faintly visible in the form of a circular depression about 20 yd in diameter just to the south of the crankshaft loading. Instead of the usual battery of buddles for concentrating the ore there was one large convex one, 50 ft (16 m) in diameter, the largest in Cornwall and said to be one of the wonders of the mine! Above the depression, between it and the path, can be seen evidence of a large pond.

(11) Early in 1994 we learned that English Heritage have refused to assist in its restoration, saying it is too far gone.

Botallack: part of the arsenic labyrinth flue built early this century.
Allen's Shaft and stack in the distance.

Left to right: Wheal Edward stamps and Cargodna 36-inch pumping-engine
houses, with the scant remains of the Cargodna steam whim. (1981)

Kenneth leading a visit at Cargodna in June 1991 - pointing out the footstep mounting for the whim cage. Below and left are holiday snapshots from 1954, kindly supplied by Lieut. Commdr. P. G. H. Richardson, showing water-powered stamps in the Kenidjack Valley.

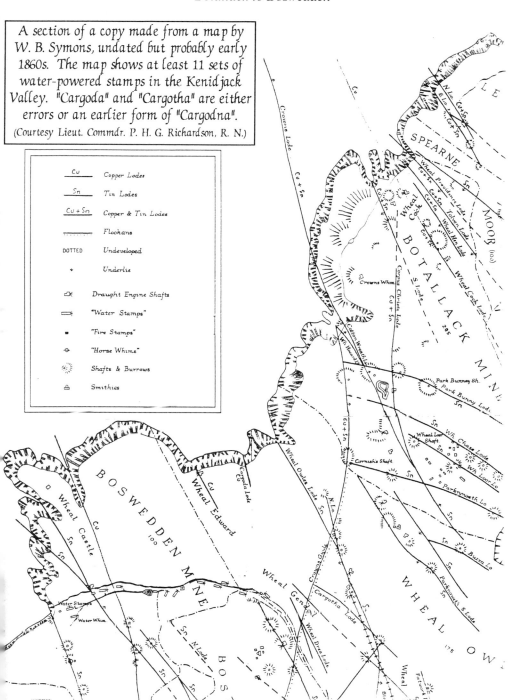

A section of a copy made from a map by
W. B. Symons, undated but probably early
1860s. The map shows at least 11 sets of
water-powered stamps in the Kenidjack
Valley. "Cargoda" and "Cargotha" are either
errors or an earlier form of "Cargodna".
(Courtesy Lieut. Commdr. P. H. G. Richardson, R. N.)

Cu	Copper Lodes
Sn	Tin Lodes
Cu + Sn	Copper & Tin Lodes
	Flookans
DOTTED	Undeveloped
•	Underlie
⋈	Draught Engine Shafts
⊏⊐	"Water Stamps"
▪	"Fire Stamps"
⊖	"Horse Whims"
☼	Shafts & Burrows
⌂	Smithies

incline shaft at the top of the cliff **(12)**. This is not readily accessible but when last seen the mouth was blocked by rubbish.

The path runs beside the remains of rifle target butts dating from about 1870-80 (information about which is given in the Cornwall Archaeological Unit's St Just Survey and in "A View from Carn Galver") before reaching the site of the Wheal Castle engine house, of which little has survived apart from the base, now overshadowed by one of the butts structures. Indeed it is easy to see why the stone from the mine's buildings was pillaged!

This ragged stump of an engine house, however, betrays one of the most remarkable chapters in Cornish mining. When Wheal Castle was being reworked briefly in 1883 it was intended that the engine should pump, by means of a short run of flat-rods, and hoist from the shaft in front of it, now only faintly visible. This old shaft, however, was found to be in such poor condition that the decision was taken to run the rods out to the cliff, then down the sheer face and back through the adit to meet the shaft. A skip road was similarly put down the cliff face. The miners had to use ladders following the same route - hazardous indeed when Force 12s were blowing! Not surprisingly the venture failed to achieve the desired object, namely to locate a supposed intersection of lodes. There is a dearth of written descriptions of this remarkable enterprise; even the celebrated local historian Cyril Noall gives it only one sentence in his "St Just Mining District"! **(13)**

The base of the engine-house stack can be discerned. The adjacent depression is where the boiler stood. At the time of writing the cylinder bedstone is still perched precariously on what is left of its loading. Behind the engine house the outline of a pond is discernible, while higher up the slope, close to the butts, can be seen the remains of a circular structure. It could mark the site of a horse whim enclosed within a building to keep out the elements, but opinions differ on this point. (The CAU's St Just Survey, for example, interprets it as a small Early Bronze Age circle.)

From this area there is a fine view across the seaward end of the Kenidjack or Nancherrow valley to Cape Cornwall; even better is the outlook, both north to Botallack Head and south to Land's End and the Wolf Rock, from the nearby small headland, known as Kenidjack Castle (because, like so many other Cornish headlands, it was the site of an Iron Age fortification), which can be approached via a rough stile at a gap in the barbed-wire fence on the seaward side of the Wheal Castle engine house. *If you do go out to the headland, when you return you could keep to the seaward side of the fence, where a rough path runs quite close to the edge of Kenidjack Quarry below - a favourite spot for new age travellers without vehicles, since wheeled access has been blocked off. Continue downhill to the main track.*

(12) The shaft descends at a steep angle to the 60-fm level where some rich bunches of tin were found. The 40-fm level here contained small amounts of pitchblende (uranium), and some of the stones in the burrow are faintly radioactive.

(13) Mr Clive Carter has found evidence among the Holman Foundry (St Just) records that the engine was used for a short time to haul stone from Kenidjack Quarry after the failure of Wheal Castle.

BOSWEDDEN MINE

It is safe to assume that miners have exploited this area for many centuries, but records go back only to 1782. Several small copper-and-tin mines such as Wheal Call (or Caul or Cole), Great Weeth and Wheal Castle operated independently or in groups during the next fifty years, finally "consolidating" as Boswedden and Wheal Castle in 1836. In 1872 a larger group including also Boscean and Wheal Cunning was formed, by the name of Wheal Cunning United, but it was short-lived. The value of the Kenidjack / Tregeseal / Nancherrow / Boswedden stream (take your pick as to its name) for operating mills, both corn and stamping, was already fully exploited by the time the Rev. John Buller wrote about St Just in his history of the parish (1840): "From this moor (Bostraze) flows a clear crystal stream of water, which maintains its purity, till it reaches the first mill in its winding course towards the sea. As it proceeds, it suspends a portion of the ochreous substance of the minerals, which are pounded and washed in numerous stamping mills to which it gives motion; till, by the time it reaches its destination, it becomes so turbid as to stain the sea ..." The Cornwall Archaeological Unit's St Just Survey estimates that the stream may have driven 50 waterwheels including those at the St Just Foundry. What was probably the largest waterwheel ever erected in Cornwall - 65 feet in diameter - was in use at Wheal Call by 1837. Almost certainly this stood down on the beach: it is hard to see where else there would have been sufficient head of water. The magnificent wheelpit that stands near the mouth of the valley now is not big enough to have contained it: that seems to have been built for a 30-ft wheel and to have been enlarged to accommodate a 52-ft wheel some time before 1865, which drove nearby buddles as well as operating pumps in two shafts by means of flat-rods. (To give you some idea of what such a wheel looked like, a drawing exists of the 54-ft wheel that was used at North Roskear Mine, near Camborne: see Volume 1 of Barton's "Essays in Cornish Mining History". This one - unlike any at Boswedden, so far as we know - was enclosed in a wooden house.) By this time the mine was exploiting mineral lodes under the sea, had a work force of 155, and employed five steam engines, two of which operated only when conditions were too dry for the waterwheels. Rather surprisingly, perhaps, Boswedden was never very profitable, and its workings were closed down soon after the amalgamation with Wheal Cunning and Boscean. The flash flood that resulted from the thaw after the Great Freeze of 1892 destroyed many of the smaller mining structures that still remained in the valley; some of the larger ones were used for demolition practice during World War 2; and the rest would probably have vanished in recent years if Geevor's plans to rework the dumps had been realised.

From this you have an excellent bird's-eye view of the remains of Boswedden Mine. A description of them follows, based on the view from this high point; in addition, for those who wish to make a closer inspection, directions for a tour of them, together with detailed descriptions, are given later. A rough scramble down the steep path which starts opposite the path down from Wheal Castle is a possible route to them for the very agile, but a safer way down is recommended, and that is described below. (See section 7, paragraph two.)

Up on the far hilltop a few overgrown burrows mark the site of the old Wheal Cunning. When reopened in the 1870s Boswedden and Wheal Castle were included in the Wheal Cunning United sett, along with Boscean (pronounced "Bosseen") Mine further up the valley. The headland away to your right can be seen to have a mine stack on its summit - if there is no sea-fog, that is. It is Cape Cornwall, the second most westerly headland in mainland England, and the old stack of Cape Cornwall Mine is maintained as a landmark for mariners. (There is little else left of the mine itself, apart from the boiler house on the south side of the Cape, now converted into a cottage.)

The horizontal tracks running along the opposite side of the valley are former leats to supply waterwheels, utilising the fast-flowing Nancherrow stream in the bottom of the valley. That they appear to run uphill is an optical illusion! The uppermost leat served a set of stamps at Cape Cornwall Mine at one time. Boswedden Mine itself was notable for the extent to which water power was used, as evinced by the massive masonry waterwheel pit which still stands by the mouth of the stream. It was built for a 30 ft diameter wheel for pumping but later extended to its present form to accommodate one of 52 ft **(14)**.

The mine's two steam engines, for pumping and stamping, were normally used only in dry weather, at times of low flow in the stream **(15)**. There were several waterwheels. The large one pumped from two shafts by flat-rods running in both directions from a crank geared to the wheel. Wheal Call Engine Shaft is the nearest to us, but being this side of the stream is concealed by a shoulder in the hillslope. It is to the left of the large waste tip, and a few remains of a steam pumping-engine survive beside this shaft. In the other direction another pumping shaft, not easily discerned from here, is on the edge of a low cliff and has partially collapsed.

The large shaft burrow up on the far hillside above the wheelpit belongs to Diagonal Shaft, which runs beneath the foreshore to a depth of 95 fm, deepest on the mine. The shaft itself is filled. Hoisting from it was effected

---

(14) The larger wheel and two steam engines were certainly in place by 1865, but an even larger waterwheel of 65 ft diameter was in use in the 1830s.

(15) Changeover from steam to water power or vice versa would have been effected as follows: The balance bob - a triangulated truss with kingpost and bridle rod stiffening - would have been permanently attached to the pump-rods in the shaft. The top length of pump-rod to the engine beam would have been made detachable, and so would the flat-rodding where it was linked to the kingpost of the balance bob. It would simply be a case of disconnecting one and connecting the other. Changing over was doubtless not as simple as it sounds, and the authors have never seen a description of how it was done.

Boswedden Mine: the fine wheel pit of dressed granite near the seaward end of the Kenidjack Valley. The courses of some of the leats that supplied water to Boswedden and Cape Cornwall Mines are clearly visible above.

by a device known as Water Whim.   This was driven through a clutch device by a 30 ft diameter waterwheel which received water from the upper leat.   Masonry remains of the wheelpit and whim mounting are visible on the hillslope.   Its tailwater was fed to the pumping wheel, thus making maximum use of the available flow.

Closer to us in the floor of the valley across the stream - usually well festooned with Japanese knotweed - are the mine's dressing floors, dominated by the ruin of the 28-inch stamps-engine house.   Its flywheel slots are clearly visible.   Partial demolition by explosives carried out as a military exercise during World War 2 left just enough to be restored recently under Penwith District Council's environmental programme. There were several small sets of waterwheel-driven stamps upstream from the engine, as illustrated by some early photographs in "A View from Carn Galver".   The dressing floors in front of the engine house have a small tunnel passing beneath, which took the flat-rods from the pumping wheel. The square, east, portal of this is visible in part of the retaining wall where the rodding crossed the stream.

Behind the stamps-engine house can be seen an open gunnis where the back (top) of the mineral lode was excavated in the mine's early days. Together with the fainter trenches running roughly parallel up the hillslope, it reveals the strike (direction) of the lodes, which run diagonally across the valley.   Similar lode-back workings on the near side of the valley can be inspected by scrambling down to them - one contains an old motor-car body - but take great care when approaching them.

7 *Turn left on the track, heading inland now.*   Ahead in the valley-bottom are the ruins of the Kenidjack arsenic works, which are so overgrown as to be inaccessible.   They are dominated by their tall, tapering chimney stack, formerly topped by a distinctive, crooked brick cowl, but this disappeared during the winter 1993 gales.   The stack served arched roasting chambers where the arsenic was driven off - the precursor of the Brunton rotating-hearth calciner, such as we saw at Botallack.   The ivy-clad buildings dotted around the works housed waterwheel-driven crushing mills.   Farther off is the prominent pumping / whim engine house of Wheal Drea (pronounced "Dray") on the left side of the valley, with the smaller remains of the Wheal Grouse stamps engine house beyond that: both parts of Wheal Owles. On the right side is a small stack that belonged to a 36-inch pumping engine on Lower Boscean Mine.

After 150 yd you will reach the point where the coastal footpath descends into the valley.   If you want to inspect Boswedden Mine more closely, this is the easiest way - otherwise, continue along the upper track for another 550 yd, and take the wide track which cuts back sharply to the left.   Pick up the directions at point 8.

To reach Boswedden, descend the coast path and turn right again at the stile on to the path close to the valley floor.   In front of you before you turn can be seen some masonry work of a large headpond which supplied water to the mine's leat system and to a more recent Pelton wheel installation near the beach.   The path now is only narrow, and can be muddy in winter and choked with knotweed in summer. As you approach the mine the stream bends very close to the path. It was here that a wooden bridge forming the main access to the mine's dressing floors etc. was swept away in a flash flood which devastated the valley in 1892, shortly after the mine had closed. All the timber work which was still standing was destroyed. About 100 yd further on the massive mounting blocks for the balance bob of Wheal Call Engine Shaft are seen beside the path on the right. The 85-fm-deep shaft, now filled, is just to the right of it, where part of the bob wall of the 37-inch pumping engine can be seen **(16)**. This engine house, too, was destroyed by the military, but on the grass-grown mound where it stood lies the cylinder bedstone with its four bolt holes, displaced from its position. The present path runs through the site of the boiler house.

As we proceed further down the path the massive waste tip towers above us to the right. Prior to the 1985 tin-price collapse, Geevor Tin Mine was negotiating lorry access to rework the tip; fortunately for the solitude of this superb mining valley the scheme was never carried out.

After passing the large wheelpit across the stream on your left, the path finishes at a rocky beach. Here traces of buddles may be seen, and across the stream the remains of a modern building in blockwork **(17)**. The buddles appear to have been driven by shafting and bevel gearing from the arched opening in the wheelpit. For the more adventurous, this is the best place to cross the stream for close inspection of the wheelpit and the two shafts.

A short climb to the wheelpit reveals its massive construction. Despite this, steps have recently been taken to reduce the ground pressure on the landward side as the wall is showing signs of bowing inwards. The cantilevered granite blocks clearly carried the outboard bearing of the pumping crank. This probably revolved at 3-4 rpm, with the wheel going at roughly half this speed.

The second pumping shaft, or Praze Shaft, is about 65 yd from the wheelpit towards the sea, where a path heading towards Cape Cornwall runs precariously on a ridge. To find it, align yourself with the edge of the cantilever blocks on the wheelpit so that the line of sight coincides with the former run of flat-rods. The shaft is left of the path where a cliff fall has occurred on the right. Immediately beyond the shaft a level "plat", circular except where part has fallen away, marks the site of a manual capstan for raising and lowering heavy pitwork. The hollow in the middle is where the winding drum was placed; traces of the rope trench to the base of the shears over the shaft are also visible. It is one of very few such capstan plats in Cornwall where its function is still discernible.

---

(16) Different sources give the cylinder size of this engine as 36, 37 and 40 inches. Bolt holes in the surviving bedstone suggest 36-37 inches and the authors believe the 37-inch figure to be correct, i.e. a 36-inch cylinder rebored to a non-standard size.
(17) Rusting machinery in the blockwork ruin is of a Pelton wheel and petrol-engined plant which is reputed to have pumped water to buildings on the hilltop. The Pelton wheel was fed from the upper leat which once served the mine; some of the pipework is still in place.

A climb up to Diagonal Shaft is rewarding only for the view from the top of the burrow. The shaft itself is only a shallow depression - that it ran out at an angle under the foreshore to a depth of 95 fm is almost impossible to visualise today.

To return to Botallack, go back along the path and follow it straight up the valley, ignoring coast path signs. On the way you will pass Kenidjack arsenic works and overgrown waterwheel installations on your right. Eventually you join a broad track on which you turn sharp left, uphill.

8 *This soon brings you past the travellers' site again.* Shortly after the sharp left turn, some rusty rails on the right side of the track mark the site of a level crossing with the horse tramway which served Kenidjack Quarry. *Return via the coast path, as before, to Botallack.*

The modern steel headgear near the car park was erected over Botallack Mine's Allen's Shaft **(18)** in the 1980s in anticipation of underground development between it and Geevor Mine's Victory Shaft. With tin prices at an all-time high, almost £10,000 a ton, the Geevor management was seeking to expand. Accordingly they purchased the headgear secondhand, and cleaned, painted and erected it along with an electric winding-engine house. The 1985 tin price collapse to around £3,000 a ton caused immediate abandonment of the project, along with several other schemes for mining rehabilitation in Cornwall.

Allen's Shaft itself is still open but protected by a timber covering and trapdoor. At the time of writing the headgear and winding house still stand as monuments to the fickle nature of mining.

---

(18) Allen's Shaft was sunk during the 1908-14 working and is a vertical, five-compartment rectangular shaft nearly 1,500 ft deep from the collar. When started, the shaft was thought to be clear of earlier mine workings but it soon encountered large quantities of water issuing from these. Although electric pumping was employed at this time, hoisting from Allen's Shaft was done by steam, a twin-cylinder horizontal winding engine being supplied by Holman Brothers of Camborne. The surviving stack served the boiler house of this engine. It later went to Taylor's Shaft of East Pool Mine near Camborne and was scrapped in 1974 after nearly 30 years idle. It should have been preserved.

GLOSSARY OF MINING & ENGINEERING TERMS USED IN THIS BOOK

Cross-references are indicated by CAPITAL LETTERS or *qv.*

Several of the terms are illustrated in Figures 1 (page 130) & 2 (page 139).

ADIT Sometimes pronounced "oddit". A drainage channel with its mouth or "portal" in a valley or on a hillside or cliff face. In deep mines, the water had to be raised by pumping to the level of the adit; this is why statistics often state the depth of a mine "below adit". Adits were often driven for exploratory purposes as well as drainage. They sometimes doubled as shafts by following the metal LODE, and provided access for the miners. Outside Cornwall adits are called levels, drifts or soughs.

ADVENTURER A shareholder in a mining enterprise.

AIR PUMP The auxiliary pump which drew condensate and air from an engine's condenser, made necessary by the vacuum formed within. It was normally in front of the engine house and worked by an independent rod from the beam.

ANGLE BOB The Cornish term for a bell-crank used to transfer horizontal motion from FLAT-RODS into the vertical motion required at a pump rod. It could be combined with a BALANCE BOB. (See sketch of a balance bob in Fig.1.) It was usually situated in a masonry pit on the edge of the shaft.

BALANCE BOB A counterpoise beam, that is, a rocking beam of timber, cast or wrought iron with one end linked to the pump rod and the other heavily weighted by a BALANCE BOX. When the rod descended the balance box's weight prevented it from falling too quickly, and when raised by the prime mover the weight helped it up. Very long, heavy pump rods would require balance bobs at several points underground as well as one at surface. Where the balance bob had a KINGPOST, the top of this could also be used to drive FLAT-RODS. (See Fig. 1.)

BALANCE BOX A wooden or iron weight box attached to one end of a BALANCE BOB and filled with rubble or iron rubbish to provide the required degree of counterbalance to the pump rod.

BALANCED (or COUNTERBALANCED) SKIPS The term applied to the use of twin skips in a hoisting shaft, attached to ropes from twin hoist cages (or drums) so that as the cages rotate, one skip is raised while the other is lowered. Hence the self weight of the skips does not affect the load being raised. (See Fig. 2.)

BEDSTONE The cylinder bedstone was a massive slab, usually of granite, to which the cylinder of a beam engine was bolted down. The bedstone (or bedstones in the case of very large engines) was (or were) placed on a deep rubble masonry foundation known as the cylinder PLAT. Bedstones were also used to support other heavy machinery items such as the beam TRUNNION bearings.

BLOWING HOUSE The early form of tin-smelting house, in which the furnace temperature was raised by bellows, usually operated by a waterwheel. The fuel used was charcoal - a principal reason for the early deforestation of Cornwall.

BOB WALL   This was the strongest wall of an engine house, which supported the bob or beam of the engine. (See sketch below.)

BRIDLE ROD   See KINGPOST.

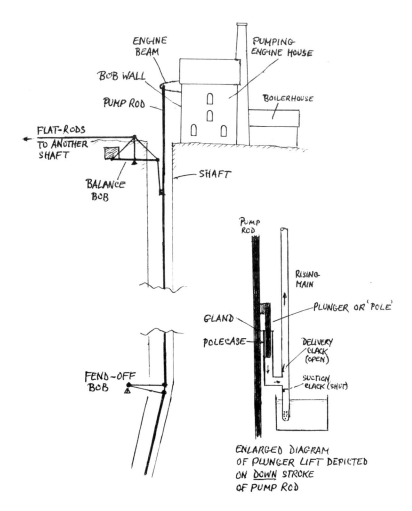

<u>Figure 1</u>

Typical arrangement of pumping engine
and plunger pump(s) in underlie shaft

130

BRUNTON CALCINER See CALCINER.

BUCKET PUMP Normally used at the bottom of the shaft in preference to a plunger pump. The bucket consists of a piston in a cylinder and raises water on the up stroke of the pump rod. A bucket pump could be moved more readily when the shaft was deepened.

BUDDLE - Concave / Convex / Dumb See Basset Mines footnote 14. The earliest form of buddle was a rectangular pit in which stamped tin was washed from its impurities by water constantly running through, and it was common practice for a boy to stand in it working with a shovel and also with his feet. By 1850, convex round buddles up to 20 feet across had come into use; the slime containing the crushed ore was fed in at the centre, and the lightest material was carried to the edges, leaving the metal near the centre. Rotating brushes were used to prevent channelling. Concave buddles, to which the slime was fed at the circumference, were used for finer material. See also ROUND FRAME and RAG (or RACK) FRAME.

BULL ENGINE A steam pumping engine which employed an inverted cylinder *(qv)* mounted directly above the shaft, thus not involving the use of a beam; for this reason this type of engine was termed "direct acting." Its invention in 1792 by Edward ("Ned") Bull led to a legal battle because Boulton and Watt claimed it infringed their separate condenser patent.

BURNING HOUSE A furnace or CALCINER (pronounced "cal-sign-er") where tin ore was made red-hot in order to burn off unwanted impurities such as sulphur and arsenic. From about 1880 when arsenic became a merchantable by-product the fumes were passed through a zigzag flue known in Cornwall as a lambreth (labyrinth), or a very long flue, or both, from which the deposits were collected.

BURROW Waste tip. Mine burrows or dumps are often very useful now as evidence of minerals produced. The burrows of many old mines have been worked over for minerals which can be recovered by improved techniques; many others have been taken away for use as building materials. Today some are being topsoiled on the grounds of high toxicity.

CAGE In Cornwall this was the term used for a winding drum on a WHIM, due to its appearance when not close-boarded. (See Fig. 2.)

CALCINER See BURNING HOUSE. A Brunton calciner employed a slowly rotating hearth so that the ore could be roasted evenly and changed over at regular intervals.

CALIFORNIAN STAMPS See STAMPS.

CAM A projection on an axle. A series of cams was used in STAMPS machines to raise and release each "lifter" in turn as the axle rotated, in a similar manner to the pin barrel in a musical box.

CAPSTAN A slow-speed winding device for raising and lowering the PITWORK in a shaft. Long arms projecting from the drum axle enabled the capstan to be operated manually, but steam capstans were also used.

CATARACT A timing device for a beam pumping engine said to have been invented by James Watt. Worked by water, in Cornwall the cataracts were normally situated in a cataract chamber or cockpit below the driver's floor, this feature being visible in many surviving engine houses today.

CLACK Non-return valve of the flap type used in PLUNGER and BUCKET LIFTS to direct the flow of water. One suction and one delivery clack are needed at each lift. (See Fig. 2.)

CLASSIFIER A device for sorting finely crushed ore mixed with water according to size. See also Basset footnote 14.

COCKPIT See CATARACT.

COFFIN, COFFEN or **GOFFEN** One of many terms used for mining on surface. A coffin or **gunnis** is a narrow, slot-like excavation; where a broader, quarry-like pit was dug the term was **openwork**. The word **stope** normally means an excavated area underground, but is also sometimes used for surface workings.

COMPOUND ENGINE A steam engine employing two cylinders, one of high and the other of low pressure. (3-cylinder compound engines existed but were not used in Cornwall.) A form of compound beam engine used in Cornwall had the high-pressure cylinder above the low-pressure, with a common piston rod. This type was known as a "combined" engine.

COMPRESSOR A machine for providing a supply of compressed air - in mines, usually for the operation of underground rockdrills.

CONDENSING WORK The condenser assembly for an engine which condensed its exhaust steam, as did all Cornish beam engines. It consisted of a receiver, pan, AIR PUMP and feed pump contained in a wooden cistern in front of the bob wall and largely submerged in cooling water drawn from a LEAT or LAUNDER.

CORNISH BOILER A cylindrical design of boiler, introduced early in the 19th century by Richard Trevithick, able to withstand much greater pressures than the older types. Cornish boilers, fitted with a single, long furnace flue, were in use on almost all Cornish mines through the rest of the century, but during the last quarter of it the Lancashire design *(qv)* began to gain favour in the County.

CORNISH ENGINE The precise definition is a beam pumping engine working on the single-acting steam cycle. (This is a modification of the cycle used in Watt-type beam engines using steam at a higher pressure, made possible by Richard Trevithick's CORNISH BOILER.) In these engines, steam applied to the top of the piston raised the pump rod and plungers in the shaft, their weight performing the return stroke. Most ROTATIVE beam engines in Cornwall were double-acting, but the term "Cornish engine" is often loosely applied to include them.

CORNISH STAMPS See STAMPS.

COUNT HOUSE Short for "account house", the mine's office. Sometimes doubled as a dwelling, and provided facilities for dinners at which adventurers and management were regaled. Count houses were often the most substantial buildings, apart from the engine houses, on the mines, and many have been converted to restaurants or small hotels or divided into several residences: the one at Wheal Buller (near the Basset Mines), for example, became six houses when the mine closed, and its present owner has applied for permission to convert it into two. Smaller mines sometimes used a shanty-type count house which could be moved to another site; the one at Wheal Charlotte, St Agnes, for instance, was moved to Porthtowan and became a seaside bungalow.

CRANKSHAFT   In a rotative beam engine, the shaft or axle of the flywheel, to which was fixed a crank, i.e. a short arm to which the "outdoor" end of the beam was attached by means of a connecting rod or "sweep rod".   In this way the reciprocating motion of the beam was converted into rotary motion for the operation of stamps or for hauling.

CROSS-COMPOUND ENGINE   A COMPOUND ENGINE in which the cylinders are arranged horizontally, but separated, side-by-side.

CRUSHER   The crushing rolls of a "Cornish crusher" were used to break down softer ores such as copper or lead.   They were usually driven by a waterwheel or clutched to a WHIM engine. Other types of crusher such as jaw and cone crushers are present-day devices for reducing rock to a predetermined size.

CYLINDER ARCH or CYLINDER DOORWAY   The door in the rear wall of an engine house - that is, opposite the BOB WALL.   It was made large enough to pass the cylinder and, in pumping engines, the beam.

DOUBLE-ACTING ENGINE   A steam engine in which both strokes of the piston in the cylinder were powered.

DRESSING FLOOR or FLOORS   The area where the large lumps of ore were broken up manually, often by boys and "bal maidens", sorted, fed to the crushers or stamps, treated in the buddles and other concentrating devices and finally calcined to remove contaminants before the metal was smelted.   (Mechanisation increasingly replaced manual methods as time passed, and other processes such as flotation and magnetic separation replaced or supplemented calcination in comparatively recent times.)

DRUM SHAFT   Shaft carrying the winding drum, or pair of drums, of a HORIZONTAL steam (or electric) winding engine.   With steam, the drum shaft was sometimes the CRANKSHAFT; alternatively it could be geared to the crankshaft or electric drive.

DRY   A building where mine workers changed their clothes - hence sometimes called a change house.   Heating was by a warming tube or pipes, often provided with steam from the engine boilers, but showers or baths were a rarity on Cornish mines.

DUTY   A measure of the efficiency of a beam engine, reckoned in terms of the weight (in lbs) of water raised one foot by the burning of one bushel of coal.   The bushel was usually 94 lb but could also be 112 lb, so in calculating an engine's efficiency it is important to know which!

EDUCTION OPENING   The aperture in the bob wall below the PLUG DOORWAY through which the eduction (exhaust) pipe passed to the condenser.

ENGINE SHAFT   A mine shaft used for the purpose of pumping, irrespective of the type of prime mover.

FATHOM   Six feet, as in nautical terminology.

FEND-OFF BOB   A pivoted device for changing the direction of the pump rods in UNDERLIE and crooked shafts. (See Fig. 1.)

FIREBAR   A bar of a fire grate.

FISHPLATE   An iron plate used in pairs to join metal bars such as rails.

FLAT-RODS   Reciprocating rods, usually of iron, which were used to transfer pumping power from an engine to a shaft remote from it. See also KINGPOST and Fig. 1.

FLYWHEEL   A large wheel with a heavy rim, used in rotative engines to achieve smooth running. See also CRANKSHAFT and Fig. 2. A STAMPS engine usually required two flywheels.

FOOTSTEP BEARING   Where a WHIM engine employed an upright axle, the axle was supported on a footstep bearing. See also MELLYER STONE.

FRUE VANNER   A device faintly resembling a large bedstead consisting of a slow-moving, endless belt on which the PULP was washed with water and at the same time agitated to separate the heavier black tin particles from the GANGUE. See also Basset Mines footnote 11.

GANGUE   Valueless minerals (rock) in the LODE from which the valuable mineral is separated.

GAUGE (of railway or tramway line)   The distance between the rails. The term "narrow gauge" refers to anything less than the "standard gauge" of 1.435 m (4 ft 8.5 in).

GUNNIS   See COFFIN.

HEADFRAME or HEADGEAR   A steel or wooden frame over the shaft to carry pulleys or sheave wheels for hoisting. See POPPET HEAD.

HEADS   See STAMPS.

HORIZONTAL ENGINE   A rotative steam engine in which the cylinder or cylinders is or are mounted horizontally, the power being applied directly to a CRANKSHAFT.

HORSE WHIM   See WHIM.

INDOOR & OUTDOOR STROKES   The "indoor stroke" of a beam engine is when the end of the beam inside the house descends. (We leave the definition of "outdoor stroke" to you!)

INVERTED CYLINDER   One in which the piston head is at the top.

KIBBLE   Old-fashioned egg-shaped bucket made of riveted wrought-iron plates by which rock was simply dragged up the shaft without guidance. The plates used to wear out quickly from the buffeting received, and repairs were a major task of the mine smithy.

KINGPOST   This was sometimes used along with "bridles" to add strength to the beam in a Cornish engine - necessary with the early wooden beams on Newcomen and Watt engines. The top of the kingpost also made a convenient point for flat-rods to be linked to an engine. A kingpost and bridles are shown in the drawing of a balance bob in Fig. 1.

LABYRINTH   See BURNING HOUSE.

LAMBRETH   See BURNING HOUSE.

LANCASHIRE BOILER   This had a shell of larger diameter than the Cornish type *(qv)*, and achieved greater flexibility by the use of twin flues. Though patented in 1844 it did not gain widespread acceptance by Cornish mines till about 1880.

LAUNDER   See LEAT.

LEAT An artificial watercourse. Where a leat was carried in a raised trough it was known as a launder.

LIFT Pump assembly fixed in the shaft. In most cases a PLUNGER lift was employed, based on a plunger pump fixed to the pump rod, but the bottom lift was usually of the BUCKET type.

LOADING A masonry or concrete platform on which machinery was mounted. See Fig. 2.

LODE A vein containing, or likely to contain, metallic ore.

LODE-BACK WORKING A shallow trench sunk only to the upper part of the lode, above the level where drainage adits or pumping would be required.

MAN-ENGINE A device used in a few very deep mines for raising and lowering men. It consisted of a rod or pair of rods moving rhythmically up and down, with steps and handholds attached. Fixed steps in the shaft at the same vertical intervals (usually 12 ft) enabled miners to step on or off the rod, thus going up or down the shaft 12 ft at a time with a single-rod engine. In a double-rod engine, miners stepped direct from one rod to the other, but in practice the machine was then so complex and risky to use that only two were ever installed. A man-engine was normally, but not invariably, worked by a beam or horizontal rotative engine at surface.

MELLYER STONE A bearing formed in a Mellyer stone supported the upright axle of a horse whim. Occasionally found built into walls and hedges.

MILL The modern term for a mine's ore-dressing plant.

OPENWORK See COFFIN.

ORE BIN A structure on surface in which ore is stored. (Underground it is known as an ore pass.)

ORE CONCENTRATION The removal of as much as possible of the waste material from metallic ore.

OVERSHOT WATERWHEEL One operated by water fed to the top of the wheel.

PELTON WHEEL A small water turbine which came into use late in the 19th century. It relied on a very good head of water to create the pressure required for efficient operation, but could operate on a low flow.

PITWORK The pumps, pump rods and other equipment used in an engine shaft.

PLAT A flat area (platform) e.g. for a horse whim; alternatively, an excavated space for a foundation, for storage of ore or for a waste tip.

PLUG DOORWAY The doorway at driver's floor level in the bob wall of an engine house.

PLUNGER PUMP A cylindrical plunger or "pole" moving up and down in a "pole case" (vessel of slightly larger diameter) displacing its own volume of water at each down stroke. Self-acting non-return valves, or "CLACKS", ensure that water is drawn into the pole case from the mine, and discharged into the RISING MAIN. (See Fig. 1.) (The bottom lift of pumps is usually of the bucket or piston type, to facilitate sinking deeper.)

POPPET HEAD See Fig. 2 and Dolcoath footnote 6.

PULP Water with particles of ore in suspension. The coarser type of pulp was often called "sands" and the finer "slimes".

RAG (or RACK) FRAME An automatic wooden device for concentrating tin ore by gravity. The slimes were fed on to a fixed wooden table, on which the heavier particles settled while light ones went to waste. The tin concentrate was then washed into a special launder by means of a trough which was continuously fed with water, toppled over when full and then righted itself to receive more water. Batteries of such frames, sometimes covering several acres, were used on dressing floors of large mines as well as by tin streamers.

REVERBERATORY CALCINER / FURNACE An improved type of tin-smelting furnace introduced into Cornwall at the start of the 18th century. It used coal and anthracite instead of wood and charcoal, and dispensed with the bellows. (See BLOWING HOUSE.) "Reverberatory" (sometimes shortened to "reverbatory") refers to the fact that the flame is turned back.

REVETMENT A retaining wall or stone facing built to support a bank of earth, cinders or other loose material.

RISING MAIN A column of pipes, usually of cast iron, flanged together, in the ENGINE SHAFT, up which water drained from the mine is forced by the pumps. (See Fig. 1.)

ROPE WALK A long narrow alley, sometimes covered, for the spinning of rope.

ROTARY ENGINE / ROTATIVE ENGINE See CRANKSHAFT, FLYWHEEL.

ROUND FRAME A device for separating black tin particles from waste material, only superficially similar to the traditional round BUDDLE. Like the RAG FRAME, it had the advantage of continuous instead of intermittent operation. The bowl itself (made of wood) rather than the brushes rotated. Round frames were used for treating very fine material.

SETT (1) The ground granted to a particular group of miners or company of adventurers - the legal boundary within which minerals could be extracted. (2) A stone (normally granite) sleeper block used to carry a rail.

SHAKING TABLE A gently inclined table over which tin-bearing PULP is passed. Mechanical vibration of the table encourages the heavier metallic particles to settle while the waste material is washed away. Common types in Cornwall were the James and Wilfley tables.

SHEARS The usual form of HEADFRAME set above a shaft, consisting of a pair of spars (shearlegs or sheerlegs) spread apart at the lower ends and joined at the top to carry a hoisting pulley for the rope from the CAPSTAN or WHIM.

SKIP ROAD, SKIPWAY The steel containers known as skips were an improvement on the "kibbles" or reinforced buckets originally used to raise material to surface, in that they were guided. Skips equipped with wheels, often known as wagons or gigs (though the latter term usually referred to man-riding wagons), were drawn up and down steep rails called skip roads or skipways.

SLIMES PLANT See PULP.

SPALLING   Breaking the big chunks of rock brought up from the mine into manageable lumps; after that came the process of "cobbing", in which the rock was hammered into a gravel-like consistency from which the worthless pieces could be picked out before the rest was fed to the crusher or stamps. A **spalling floor** was a level cobbled area, still discoverable at a few mines, on which the lumps of rock were broken down. The manual breaking up of rock was typical of copper rather than tin mines.

STAMPS   **Cornish Stamps** machines were used to crush the small lumps of ore into material like sand in texture. Heavy timber or iron lifters with iron "heads" at the bottom were raised by CAMS on a rotating axle, and fell on the ore-and-water mixture, fed into a box beneath. The heads normally weighed between 4 and 8 cwts each, and were usually arranged in sets of four, in timber frames. Small stamps were commonly powered by water-wheels and larger ones by steam engines.
Californian Stamps, developed for use in the Californian gold mines, began to appear in Cornwall towards the end of the 1880s. They worked on the same principle but were more rapid in action, and the heads (up to half a ton in weight) and lifters were made to rotate so that they wore more evenly.

STAMPS AXLE   A hollow cast- or wrought-iron shaft rotated by a stamps engine or waterwheel and having square holes for insertion of the stamps CAMS.

STEAM CASE (or STEAM JACKET)   To avoid excessive heat-loss, the cylinder in a Cornish beam engine was usually provided with an outer case, occasionally an old cylinder of slightly larger diameter, the intervening space being fed with live steam and with a drain leading back to the boiler(s). This is why the boiler(s) was/were normally placed below the level of the cylinder bottom. Outside the steam case was an insulating layer consisting of ashes or felt and surrounded with brickwork or wooden casing.

STOPE   See COFFIN.

STREAMING   The normal method of winning tin before deep mining became possible, and practised in recent times in several places, such as the Bissoe valley, and on a small scale at the seaward end of Trevellas Coombe. Tin washed down into valleys and buried under layers of silt (i.e. detrital tin) was exposed, originally by shovel and wheelbarrow; the tin-bearing gravel was then sorted and washed, and the waste material used to back-fill the excavated area. Tin streaming was often done as a family concern, using simple waterwheel-driven equipment, and such operations mushroomed along streams carrying tin-bearing waste from the larger mines. Nowadays, earth-movers and lorries take that same material to plants where modern methods are able to extract the valuable minerals still present.

SUMP   The bottom of the engine shaft, from which the lowest lift of pumps draw.

TAILINGS   The waste material from the dressing processes, which in less environmentally-conscious days was merely discharged into the nearest river or stream or the sea. In modern tin mines the tailings, mixed with water, are pumped into a lagoon or tailings dam and allowed to settle; eventually the water may be re-used by the mine, and the tailings are sometimes re-processed at a later date when higher prices or improved technology make this worthwhile. Finally - at least in theory - the dried-out reservoir is grassed over.

TAILRACE The leat or launder which carries away the water from a waterwheel - sometimes back to the stream, sometimes to another wheel at a lower level.

TRAMROAD, TRAMWAY In the context of Cornish mining history these terms are generally reserved for mineral railways built to connect various sites within a mine or group of mines, but are sometimes used for horse-drawn systems as opposed to those employing locomotives. The Redruth & Chasewater Railway was so-called, however, even in its early days of horse traction, and the Basset and Dolcoath Tramways kept that name even when steam locos took over from the horses. South Crofty used a horse tram into the 1950s, linking the two shafts.

TRUNNION A shaft supporting a rocking beam (or bob) near or at its centre, the projecting ends of which rest in **trunnion bearings** which enable the beam to pivot.

TWO-STAGE In more modern air compressors the air is compressed twice, in two cylinders successively.

UNDERLIE Mineral LODES in Cornwall are very rarely vertical, but "underlie" or "dip" by a certain number of degrees. Similarly, the typical shaft until quite late in the history of Cornish mining followed the lode, and its angle of deviation from the vertical is known as the underlie of the shaft.

UNDERSHOT WATERWHEEL One operated by water running beneath it.

VALVE GEAR The mechanism which operates the steam and exhaust valves of a steam engine. Since a Cornish beam pumping engine has no rotary motion, its valve gear consists of a fascinating array of deadweights, trips and handles (for starting) and is known as **gearwork**.

VANNER See FRUE VANNERS, SHAKING TABLES and Basset Mines footnote 11. "Vanning" is the old term for using a shovel to wash tin particles from waste material, or to test the concentration of ore in a sample.

WASH WATER The flow of water carrying the ore and waste rock particles through the various dressing processes.

WEIGHPOST See Consols footnote 2.

WHIM, WINDING ENGINE A machine for hoisting water, ore or other heavy materials from the mine. The earliest whims were operated manually or by horses. In **horse whims**, the animal walked round and round turning a wooden cage (drum) around which was wound the cable attached to the KIBBLE or bucket. Horse whims continued in use by small mines until this century. **Water whims** were used in a few Cornish mines where the hoisting mechanism was clutched to an axle driven by a water-

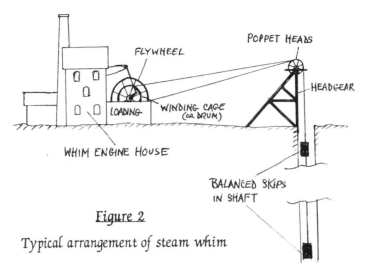

Figure 2

Typical arrangement of steam whim

wheel.   The whims in deep mines were driven by beam engines, as illustrated in the sketch above, and in the early 19th century these were sometimes known as **fire whims**.   Some worked on the old horse-whim principle of having an upright axle for the cage.   In Cornwall, beam engines were superseded by horizontal steam whims much later than in coal-mining districts, some working well into this century.

WING WALLS The side walls of an engine house - often among the first parts of disused engine houses to collapse as a result of the removal or rotting of roof trusses and internal joinery.

A NOTE FOR MINERAL COLLECTORS

by Cedric Rogers

(author of *A Collector's Guide to Minerals, Rocks and Gemstones in Cornwall & Devon*)

The various mining sites covered in this book will have a special appeal for anyone interested in mineral collecting. Most of them would at some time in the past have been promising areas for prospecting for specimens ("fossicking", to use the Australian expression, or "rock hunting" as the Americans call it), some being richer and more varied than others of course.

Thirty years ago there were still many waste heaps that were almost as fresh as when they were last in use. Collectors could pick up a bag full of representative specimens without too much trouble. Now the picture is rather different and the easy pickings become fewer as each year goes by.

Several factors are responsible for the loss of good collecting sites. Some of the best became housing or industrial estates while others have been returned to farm land. Those mines which have been preserved are of industrial archaeological interest and have often been tidied up and landscaped out of recognition, while those which have been passed over have usually become overgrown. Some of these changes can take place almost overnight.

For these reasons it is not possible to give more than a very generalised account of what minerals might be found in any given area. However, minerals are still there and many dumps are still good for specimens as long as you are short on expectations and long on patience. One should look out for any signs of recent excavation. Small diggings are often the signs of other collectors and could indicate a lucky strike. Others may be the work of rabbits, but look them over anyway! In fact good specimens may be only inches from where you are standing - below the surface.

Dump material: Country Rock, Gangue and Ore Minerals

(Names of minerals printed in italics are included in a brief glossary at the end of this note.)

Country rock is simply the predominant rock or rocks of the area in which the mining takes place. Most common in Cornwall are granite and killas (the local name for various slates and shales).

Gangue is that part of the veinstone (or lode) which has no commercial value, the waste material after the ore has been separated and concentrated. Typical of gangue materials are *quartz, chlorite, fluorite,* and *schorl* (black *tourmaline).* Some gangue minerals may, in a different context, be mined in their own right, such as *pyrite, arsenopyrite* and *wolframite* (tungsten). Often these minerals (e.g. crystals of quartz, fluorite and pyrite) may themselves be highly desirable as collector's items, and certainly they are more likely finds.

Ore minerals are what it is all about! But very hard to find these days. Anything that escaped the net of the sorting tables will have to have eluded the eyes of generations of other collectors. The chief ores of Cornwall are those of tin (*cassiterite* is the only one) and copper, with the *sulphides* (*chalcopyrite, chalcocite* and *bornite)* and the oxide *(cuprite)* heading a longer list. Other metals have been mined in Cornwall but not significantly at those mines covered in this book.

Dumps

Dump material varies from mine to mine. The few dumps that have remained unaltered, apart from weathering and overgrowth, will usually retain a pattern of deposits. The creation of a mature dump is the result of various distinct operations. First come the topsoil, gravel and country rock that must be removed to gain access to the lodes. Then once the mining operations are under way a great deal more waste rock is constantly being dug out to create access and working space, shafts, adits, ventilation and so on. Dumps which contain defined boundaries between topsoil, gravel and country rock may reveal patches of veinstone material. When this happens it is time to narrow the search, although, as already mentioned, gangue materials often contain collectable crystals themselves - in fact, they are usually the better bet. Another part of the same dump may be simply a heap of mining rubbish - cinders and slag from boilers, rusted iron, bricks, concrete, old wood, rags and perhaps a fossil pasty crust or two.

Alterations to the original dump may be the result of various operations. Early sorting methods resulted in a high proportion of ore being overlooked and ending up on the waste tips. Later operations often concentrated on reprocessing the earlier waste itself. The dumps are frequently "quarried" for filling material and so on. When this has happened recently it is always worth checking over for signs of minerals which may not have seen daylight for many years.

A recent and exciting development has been the blossoming of interest in our industrial past. One doesn't have to go very far back in time to find widespread indifference to the fate of the old mine buildings. Until quite recently guide books to Cornwall would completely ignore their existence, as if they were skeletons in the family cupboard. Visitors would come and go assuming they were a local kind of castle. To the Cornish as a whole they might seem unsightly reminders of a lost prosperity. Thankfully, enough dedicated people have applied themselves to stopping and in a modest way reversing the rot by restoring the masonry of some of the most worthy cases. Inevitably, in the process of tidying up the site and landscaping the surrounds for aesthetic reasons the dumps, whose beauty is restricted to the eyes of beholders who happen to be "rockhounds" (another Americanism), are flattened and grassed over. When a once promising tip has been bulldozed over several acres the task of finding anything collectable becomes purely a matter of luck.

Blue-Green Copper Minerals

Wherever copper has been in evidence traces of blue or green staining are commonly seen among the rocks of the vicinity - as specks and smudges, or even as great splashes of colour coating cliff faces or the walls of caves. These usually indicate the presence of any one of literally dozens of secondary copper minerals. Obviously it would be impossible for a casual observer to try to identify which one, unless a stain was backed up by more substantial signs of the mineral's presence, such as crystals. However, a green stain may be the green light to look closer and dig deeper: a recent visit to the Marriott's Shaft section of South Wheal Frances, for example, was rewarded when a glimpse of bright green led to the discovery of a chunk of rock with cherry red cuprite, native copper and *malachite.*

Books

For those of you whose interest in minerals is whetted by *Exploring Cornish Mines* we strongly advise you to seek out books which can tell you more about them than can be described here. For those interested specifically in Cornish minerals the best book is undoubtedly *Minerals of Cornwall and Devon* by Embrey and Symes, published for the British Museum (Natural History). Although it doesn't go into mineral recognition it does illustrate some of the more exotic specimens found in Cornwall, and seldom seen in more generalised books. But don't expect to find anything like them these days unless you have Aladdin's lamp in your collecting bag. Much more modest but perhaps more to the point is the little paperback referred to at the start of these notes, which I wrote back in the '60s, strictly for absolute beginners, focusing on the more likely finds in the West Country. Although it has been out of print for some time it is being updated and, I hope, republished in the near future.

DESCRIPTIVE GLOSSARY OF MINERALS

Cross-references are indicated by *(qv)*.

Arsenopyrite   A gangue mineral associated with wolfram. A sulphide *(qv)* of iron and steely-grey, silvery-grey on fracture face. Garlicky smell when struck with hammer. Also mined as an ore of arsenic.

Bornite   A sulphide *(qv)* of copper and iron, not as common as chalcopyrite but a valuable ore. "Horseflesh ore", bronze colour on fresh fracture surface, tarnishes quickly to purple.

Cassiterite   "Black tin." Crystals are normally a glittering black but may shade into brown or cream. Distinctively heavy. Darkish rock that feels unduly heavy may well be rough tin ore.

Chalcocite   Next to chalcopyrite *(qv)* this is the main copper ore of Cornwall. A straight sulphide *(qv)* of copper, it is dark lead-grey on the outside, fracture face steely lustre. The major ore of copper in the St Just area.

Chalcopyrite   "Yellow copper ore". May be confused with pyrite *(qv)* if crystals are absent, as they usually are, but the practised eye can tell from the yellowness which is which. Chalcopyrite is a distinctly brassy yellow with frequent iridescent tarnishing. Pyrite is paler.

Chlorite　A fairly common gangue mineral, an earthy green colour of no great eye-appeal.

(Native) Copper　The real McCoy, unadulterated, as found in nature. Usually with green (verdigris) coating. Often in thin plates or knobbly and twig-like.

Cuprite　Red oxide of copper. This is a lesser ore but good collectors' material. Deep carmine red, metallic lustre on fresh surface. Crystals are usually simple octahedrons (double-ended pyramids). Usually with dark tarnish.

Fluorite　is a common gangue mineral which also has economic importance, e.g. as a flux in the steel industry. Comes in all colours of the spectrum, particularly pale straw, aquamarine and deep amethyst. Transparent to translucent, conspicuous cleavage and cubic crystals make identification easy.

Malachite　More common than azurite *(qv)*. Its colour, a rich, velvety green, is well known from its use as a decorative, semiprecious stone. Often encountered as one of those anonymous green copper stains.

Pyrite　The commonest sulphide *(qv)* (of iron) and well known as "fool's gold" for obvious reason. See also chalcopyrite.

Quartz　The commonest of all minerals. Crystals of all sizes are widespread in Cornwall. It is the stuff of many gemstones, notably agate, amethyst, carnelian and citrine, but most likely to be found as milk-white or iron-stained chunks and pebbles or even whole boulders, originating as veinstone.

Schorl　Black tourmaline *(qv)*, common gangue material and in certain granites. Crystals are black and needle-like, typically embedded in white quartz. *(qv)*.

Sulphides　The name for a distinctive chemical group of minerals which predominate among the ores. Their common feature is, apart from sphalerite, that they virtually all have the lustre of polished metal.

Tourmaline　A colourful gemstone, rarely found as such in Cornwall.

Wolframite　occurs with quartz *(qv)* and arsenopyrite *(qv)* as a gangue material, but may also be mined as an ore of tungsten. Slablike, black crystals the size of dominoes are not uncommon. Usually displays one or two shiny fracture faces.

IMPORTANT NOTE

Please bear in mind that no-one has the automatic right to take minerals from privately- (or even publicly-) owned land, and that there are specific restrictions or bans in force regarding mineral collecting on, for example, SSSIs (Sites of Special Scientific Interest), RIGSs (Regionally Important Geological Sites) and National Trust property. Avoid trespassing. Most people will give permission for mineral collectors to explore their property if presented with a courteous request.

BIBLIOGRAPHY

Atkinson, R. L., *Copper and Copper Mining,* Shire Publications, Aylesbury, 1976
Atkinson, R. L., *Tin and Tin Mining,* Shire Publications, Aylesbury, 1985
Barton, D. B., *The Cornish Beam Engine,* D.B.Barton, Truro, 1965
Barton, D. B., *Essays in Cornish Mining History* (2 volumes), D.B.Barton, Truro, 1968/1971
Barton, D. B., *A History of Copper Mining in Cornwall and Devon,* D.B.Barton, Truro, 1961
Barton, D. B., *A History of Tin Mining and Smelting in Cornwall,* D.B.Barton, Truro, 1965
Barton, D. B., *The Redruth & Chasewater Railway,* D.BBarton, Truro,1961
Buckley, J. A., *Cornish Mining - at Surface,* Tor Mark Press, Penryn, 1990
Buckley, J. A., *The Cornish Mining Industry, a Brief History,* Tor Mark Press, Penryn, 1992
Collins, J. H., *Observations on the West of England Mining Region,* 1912
      (Facsimile edition, Cornish Mining Classics, Truro, 1988)
Dines, H. G., *The Metalliferous Mining Region of South-West England* (2 volumes), HMSO,
      London, 1956
Earl, Bryan, *Cornish Mining: The Techniques of Metal Mining in the West of England, Past*
      & Present, D.B.Barton, Truro, 1968 (New edition due from Cornish Hillside Pub.)
Harris, T. R., *Dolcoath - Queen of Cornish Mines,* Trevithick Society, 1974
Henwood, George, *Cornwall's Mines and Miners* (1857-9), D. B. Barton, Truro, 1972
Jenkin, A. K. Hamilton, *The Cornish Miner,* George Allen & Unwin, 1927
Jenkin, A. K. Hamilton, *Mines and Miners of Cornwall:*
      II - *St Agnes - Perranporth,* Truro Bookshop, 1962
      III - *Around Redruth,* Truro Bookshop, 1962
      VI - *Around Gwennap,* Truro Bookshop, 1963
      X - *Camborne and Illogan,* Truro Bookshop, 1965
Leifchild, J. R., *Cornwall, Its Mines and Miners,* Longman, London, 1857
      (Facsimile edition, Frank Cass, London, 1968)
Morrison, T. A., *Cornwall's Central Mines - The Southern District, 1810-1895,* Alison
      Hodge, Penzance, 1983
Noall, Cyril, *Botallack,* D. B. Barton, Truro, 1972
Noall, Cyril, *Cornish Mining Disasters,* Dyllansow Truran, 1989
Noall, Cyril, *The St Just Mining District,* D. B. Barton, Truro, 1973
Orchard, W. G. (ed.), *A Glossary of Mining Terms,* Dyllansow Truran, 1991
Ordish, H. G., *Cornish Engine Houses, A Pictorial Survey,* D. B. Barton, Truro, 1967
Ordish, H. G., *Cornish Engine Houses, A Second Pictorial Survey,* D.B.Barton, Truro, 1968
Palmer, M., & Neaverson, P., *The Basset Mines, Their History & Industrial Archaeology,*
      Northern Mine Research Society, 1987
Pascoe, W. H., *C.C.C., The History of the Cornish Copper Company,* Dyllansow Truran, 1981
Rogers, Cedric, *A Collector's Guide to Minerals, Rocks and Gemstones in Cornwall &*
      Devon, D. B. Barton, Truro, 1968
Sharpe, A. *et al., Engine House Assessment - Mineral Tramways Project,* Cornwall
      Archaeological Unit, 1991
Sharpe, A., *The Red River Trail: An Archaeological Assessment,* Cornwall
      Archaeological Unit, 1990
Sharpe, A., *St Just - An Archaeological Survey of the Mining District* (2 volumes),
      Cornwall Archaeological Unit, 1992
Sharpe, A., & Smith, J., *Trevellas, St Agnes, Cornwall: An Archaeological Survey,*
      Cornwall Archaeological Unit, 1986
Stanier, Peter, *Cornwall's Mining Heritage,* Twelveheads Press, Truro, 1988
Trounson, J. H., *Cornish Engines & the Men who Handled Them,* Trevithick Society, 1985
      (reprinted from the Journal of the Royal Institution of Cornwall, 1967)
Trounson, J. H., *The Cornish Mineral Industry 1937-1951,* University of Exeter, 1989
Trounson, J. H., *Cornwall's Future Mines,* University of Exeter, 1993
Trounson, J. H., *Historic Cornish Mining Scenes at Surface,* D.B.Barton,Truro, no date
Trounson, J. H., *Mining in Cornwall,* Vol. 1, Dyllansow Truran, Redruth, 1980
Trounson, J. H., *Mining in Cornwall,* Vol. 2, Moorland, Derbyshire, 1982